DATE DUE

JA 05'05			
FEB 27 08			
GAYLORD			PRINTED IN U.S.A.

MEDIC

Books by Eloise Engle

MEDIC: *America's Medical Soldiers, Sailors and Airmen in Peace and War*

EARTHQUAKE! *The Story of Alaska's Good Friday Disaster*

SKY RANGERS: *Satellite Tracking Around the World (with Kenneth H. Drummond)*

PARARESCUE: *What Men Dare Do*

ESCAPE: *From the Air and from the Sea*

MEDIC

America's Medical Soldiers, Sailors and Airmen in Peace and War

Eloise Engle

ILLUSTRATED

The John Day Company   New York

For Erick Berry, editor. And we are still friends after this, our tenth book together.

Contents

Acknowledgments

THIS book began four years ago when I was doing research on a novel for girls, entitled *Dawn Mission,* an account of the heroic work of Air Force flight nurses and med techs who were assigned to aeromedical evacuation teams during the Korean conflict. At that time I flew air evac from Washington, D.C., to Seoul, Korea, in order to observe the air-evac system firsthand and to interview the men and women who cared for patients in flight. I was greatly impressed with the responsibilities, the skill and dedication to duty of the enlisted aeromedical technicians. I began to take notes on the general subject, and subsequently on other trips and assignments I sought out enlisted medics of all three branches of the service in order to learn more about their breed: their experiences, training and duties, both now and in the past. I found these men when I was researching for a book about the development of escape systems (*Escape*) and again when studying the work of the Air Force's Pararescuemen (*Pararescue*), and the files for *Medic* continued to grow.

Research for this book has been difficult, but rewarding. Difficult because no account of the enlisted medics of the Army, Navy and Air Force medical departments had yet been compiled and because of the enormous scope I wanted to cover. For instance, one outstanding medic whose story I arbitrarily chose to tell could be multiplied by thousands; one heroic action could only illustrate what had been happening through the years in all parts of the world.

But there were the rewards. Everyone with whom I talked was anxious to help me act upon my personal conviction that this account was long overdue and most certainly deserved to be written.

The medical departments of the armed services were most cooperative in sending out an "SOS" in their newsletters. Responses from medics all over the world poured in. Personal letters and tape recordings filled in many informational gaps. The public information officers worked hard to assist with photos, news releases, background material and the setting up of interviews. Lieutenant Colonel William Mullens, MSC, with the Army Surgeon General's office, Lieutenant Norman Peckenpaugh, MSC, with the Navy Surgeon General's office, and Pat Bragg at the Air Force Surgeon General's office worked with me on a continuing basis. At the Pentagon, my good friends Major B. J. Smith, Lieutenant Commander Dan Dagle and Colonel C. V. Glines were always on hand for help. My trip to Germany to talk with medics at Frankfurt, Wiesbaden and Heidelberg was highlighted by an efficient and delightful P.I.O., Major Elizabeth Slawson at Heidelberg, and a cordial reunion with Colonel "Chip" Bergwin at Wiesbaden. Lieutenant Colonel James Sunderman at PACAF supplied excellent material on current air-evac activities in Southeast Asia. Lieutenant Colonel Alfred Yamazaki at Fort Totten, New York, arranged for a long session with Charles Short, whose story is prominent in this book.

No strong lines were drawn as to who would talk with me on the subject of medics. I wanted the opinions of those who were responsible for these enlisted men, so I talked with Vice Admiral Robert B. Brown, who is Surgeon General of the Navy, and with Major General Kenneth Pletcher, Deputy Surgeon General of the Air Force. And I wondered what the man who is now in charge of all the Marines in Vietnam would have to say about his enlisted corpsmen. Major General Lewis Walt responded with a fantastic briefing, based on his experiences with them in the South Pacific during World War II, in Korea and now in Vietnam. On the scene in Vietnam, Captain Bruce Canaga, MC, USN, and Commander Al Wilson, MC, USN, supplied photos and on-the-spot information.

And then there were the interviewees themselves: the medics and corpsmen and med techs whose experiences are related in this book. Often it was difficult for these men to talk about things they wanted to forget, and there were times when we would pause because the words did not want to come out. But we wanted the truth, no matter how painful . . . so we kept at it.

Various publications were generous with their material. *Army Magazine, All Hands* and *Leatherneck,* along with the *Hospital Corps Quarterly,* were extremely useful to me. Chief Warrant Officer Hal Rice supplied tips, information and encouragement from the very beginning. Patricia Bergman managed to get hold of obscure publications from the Congressional Library for me to browse through.

Finally, my thanks to Erick Berry, to whom this book is dedicated, and to Richard Walsh for having faith in it.

E.E.

Falls Church, Virginia.

MEDIC

1

An Aidman in Korea

IN a way, nineteen-year-old Private First Class Richard G. Wilson, Medical Company, 187th Airborne Infantry Regiment, could have been described as a "young, old man" because of what he had seen and done since he arrived in Korea in 1950. As medical aidman attached to Company I, he had seen comrade after comrade fall in the field of battle; although he had done what he could to save them, there were too many who were beyond help.

As days had turned into weeks, his buddies began to notice the tired, haggard lines forming on the young medic's face, and they kidded him about it. No one mentioned the strange, almost haunted look he sometimes had in his eyes because they all had it—one way or another.

PFC Wilson welcomed any ribbing he got as a sign that the ribbers were still among the living. And as he performed his foxhole surgery, stopped bleeding, administered plasma and antibiotics, gave shots of morphine and struggled to get his wounded charges away from the front line to the aid station, his banter was as cocky, indignant and unsympathetic as he dared make it. The men in the regiment knew this, and understood. Not much goes unnoticed among men who live, train, work, jump, fight and play together. Few kept any secrets from the medic. They told him about their wives, their kids and their sweethearts. They cursed him when they were in pain and wept when they were afraid. But that was all right. The medic knew how to keep his mouth shut. He did a good job and was somehow around whenever the going got rough.

In most ways PFC Wilson was no different from the rest of the paratroopers in his regiment. He had been through the rugged Airborne School at Fort Benning, Georgia, and had collected the same decorations and awards: Distinguished Unit Emblem; Korean Service Medal with Bronze Arrowhead for the invasion of Sunchon-Sukchon, October 20, 1950, and one Bronze Service Star for the United Nations Offensive Campaign; National Defense Service Medal; United Nations Service Medal; Parachute Badge and Glider Badge.

Before he was sent to Korea, the Army had taught him many things: how to protect himself, seek shelter, recognize terrain, read maps, follow contours of the land and find coordinates. He had learned how to flatten his body and crawl along the ground; he had a fairly good knowledge of chemical warfare. In training he had become accustomed to the nerve-shattering explosion of bomb and shell, to detecting angles of fire, to traversing the depths of areas undergoing violent bombardment, and to ascertaining the points of danger and relative safety. For he was a part of the fighting machine, even though he had no gun.

What distinguished him from the others was the combat medical badge he wore. At Fort Sam Houston he'd been taught to render first aid to battle casualties. To do this he could not remain in the rear area until needed, but rather stayed close to those for whom he was responsible, whether on the march or in actual combat.

No one thought of PFC Wilson as a medical doctor; he was a medical soldier, and that was that. He had no scientific degree, and he had done no research in a steaming jungle or in a fine medical laboratory. He did not have elaborate instruments or an array of drugs to help him to care for the sick and injured. Yet to each soldier entrusted to his care, PFC Wilson was the entire Army Medical Service. His medical kit was his total equipment; his medical training was being completed on the field of battle.

In Korea, he got very weary, because there was always so much to do. The winter was a bitter one, and he was cold and worn most of the time, yet he dared not let up. And so, at the end of the day when the drill, march or battle was done, PFC Wilson would break out the medications: the aspirin, bandaids, bandages, Merthiolate and antibiotics. He would check over the unfit, rub sore muscles, dress blisters, treat dysenteries and spray DDT on lice and other parasites that pestered his men. On October 21, 1950, he went out, as usual, with his unit as it made a reconnaissance through the hilly country near Opari. The terrain was tricky and required the utmost caution, but a look-see at what the enemy was up to was an absolute must. The countryside, though primitive and somewhat dreary, was ominously quiet as the unit marched into a narrow valley that was flanked on three sides by high hills. And then . . .

PHOOM!

Bursts of mortar fire came from the hills as the enemy loosed its murderous barrage. Automatic weapons and small arms showered death and destruction into the unit's midst. Men fell, bleeding from their wounds; others scrambled for cover. Someone shouted "Ambush!" The unit now began to fight to get out of that hellhole.

But PFC Wilson had work to do. There were the wounded to care for, men who called "Medic" or "Hey, Doc," who groaned quietly or just lay still. Somehow as he crawled or ran from one injured man to another—tying, splinting, injecting morphine . . . and God, the blood, would it never stop flowing?—he was dimly aware of the bullets pinging near him, the explosions of gre-

Private First Class Richard G. Wilson, Army medic, Medal of Honor winner who gave his life for others in Korea.

nades as they chewed up that valley of death, of the bucket-swishing roar of mortar; and he wondered if he would get his this time, just as these men he was trying to save had got theirs. Some of the men he had known so well clung to him as a child does to its mother, and sometimes Wilson found himself kneeling beside a G.I. and saying a prayer as the dying man slipped away on his last journey.

With the enemy threatening to encircle and isolate the company, the commander ordered a withdrawal. Now Wilson did what he could to get his wounded to safety. Volunteer litter bearers, big G.I. shoulders—all were called on to get the casualties out. Wilson mentally tallied them all; everyone was accounted for as the unit moved out.

Once established in a safe area, the young medic from Missouri checked his patients again: tighten the bandage, start some plasma to ward off shock, break out the syrettes of morphine . . .

He worked until he nearly dropped from fatigue, but there were no limitations on saving lives. You just kept going.

Someone said, "Where's Rogers?" and PFC Wilson explained sadly that the man was dead.

"But I saw him moving! He was trying to crawl away to safety."

PFC Wilson straightened up and took a deep breath. A shiver ran through his body as he remembered that hideous holocaust they had just left, the grisly sight of his mangled comrades. But there was no choice—no choice at all. He picked up his aid kit and slung it over his shoulder. "I'll go back for him," he said slowly. He could never live with the thought that Rogers had been left behind, possibly still alive and needing help.

"But you can't go back! You'll get it, just like the others. The place is crawlin' with gooks!" the men told him.

"Don't worry. I won't be long."

Two days later a patrol found PFC Richard Wilson. He was lying beside the man he had returned to help, and it was obvious to the men on the patrol that their medic had tried to shield the wounded man with his own body as he administered aid. The enemy's shots at the unarmed man had been fatal.

On June 21, 1951, Private First Class Richard G. Wilson, Medical Company, 187th Airborne Infantry Regiment, was given the nation's highest award, the Medal of Honor (posthumous), "for conspicuous gallantry and intrepidity above and beyond the call of duty. . . . Private Wilson's superb personal bravery, consummate courage and willing self-sacrifice for his comrades reflect untold glory upon himself and uphold the esteemed traditions of the military service."

2

The Early Army Medical Soldier

"When you're wounded and left on Afghanistan's plains,
And the women come out to cut up what remains,
Just roll to your rifle and blow out your brains,
An' go to your Gawd like a soldier. . . ."

Rudyard Kipling
"The Young British Soldier"

ALTHOUGH medical aid of sorts for troops existed since the earliest wars, it was intended mainly for senior officers. Up until the fifteenth century the wounded soldier got very little consideration. Usually he was left behind to be cared for by the local population, or a buddy would put him out of his misery with the knife in order to avoid torture by the enemy. British Army medical history shows that during the reign of Edward II, there was only one "chirurgeon" (surgeon)—whose pay was four pence a day—for every 1,900 men. There was but one doctor for Edward III's entire force besieging Calais. In Henry V's military code, physicians ranked after shoemakers and tailors, but before washerwomen. In warrants authorizing the levy of surgeons in Elizabeth's reign, they were usually coupled with drummers. Medical aidmen had not even been thought of.

The recognized treatment of gunshot wounds in those days was cauterization with boiling oil of elders mixed with treacle (molasses). Some curious, revolting balms were also used; one was concocted from two young whelps boiled alive and two pounds of earthworms purified in white wine. Boiling pitch was used to stop bleeding after amputation.

The formation of the standing British Army brought a limited system of regimental surgeons and hospitals, but medical aid for expeditionary forces remained rudimentary. This condition, along with the terrible and crippling losses from yellow fever, bubonic plague, dysentery and typhus (the remedy for typhus was port wine and Peruvian bark—quinine), brought cries of protest from physicians and military strategists alike, yet not much was done to alleviate the situation. Wellington was infuriated by the suggestion that some vehicles be set aside to transport casualties to hospitals, but Sir James McGrigor, the Iron Duke's Inspector of Hospitals, still managed to establish a chain of hospitals all along the route to Salamanca and used the commissary transport to evacuate the wounded. He also arranged for wooden hospital buildings to be sent out, ready-made, from home. They were, in fact, the world's first prefabricated hospitals.

The history of the American Army Medical Service* began during the siege of Boston in 1775, when wounded patriots suffered horribly for lack of medical care. After the Battle of Bunker Hill in June, General Gage, British military governor of Massachusetts, made no provision for the wounded; there were dead and wounded officers on every street and no one desig-

---

* Originally called the United States Army Hospital Corps, it became known as the Army Medical Department in 1887. It retained this name until July 26, 1947, when the National Security Act provided for the Army Medical Service.

nated to remove them. Boston, which was at that time larger than New York, became virtually deserted. Hour after hour, the bells tolled grimly while wounded soldiers lying in tents called for someone to come and remove the dead. A few wounded officers found lodgings in private homes—at exorbitant fees—but the majority of men suffered unnoticed and uncared for. This situation remained for three days, until indignant physicians and townspeople demanded something be done. As a result, several hospitals were established in private homes.

In July, when the Continental Congress appointed George Washington to be Commander-in-Chief and provided for the appointment of general officers and officers for a general staff, there was still no provision for a hospital or medical department. It was on General Washington's first inspection that plans for soldiers' medical care began to take shape. On July 21 he wrote to the President of Congress, "I have made enquirey into the establishment of the hospital and find it in a very unsettled condition. . . . I could wish it was immediately taken into consideration as the lives and health of both officers and men so much depend on a due regulation of this department."

Congress responded with "an hospital" to be established for the army of 20,000 men. Its staff consisted of one Director General and a Chief Physician, four surgeons, one apothecary, twenty surgeon's mates, one clerk, two storekeepers, one nurse for every ten sick, and laborers occasionally as needed. There was very little money to support the project and even less interest on the part of the personnel. But it was a start.

Before long, every regiment had set up a hospital, though it more resembled a jail than a house for healing. Each consisted of two small rooms, one above the other. Twelve men were tended in each, so the rooms were almost one continuous bed. Only the worst cases were sent to the "hospital," and there was no segregation of patients suffering from the horrible diseases of the day: fevers, jaundice, dropsy, vomiting, cholera morbus,

Reproduction of hospital hut built on the original site, occupied 1777–78 at Valley Forge, Pennsylvania. *U.S. Signal Corps Photo in the National Archives*

diarrhea, dysentery, scurvy, itch, worms, smallpox, typhoid, tuberculosis, pneumonia and others. There was no such thing as diagnosis, pathology, epidemiology, or hygiene of any sort. Treatment for any and all diseases was the latest for the year 1775: bleeding, warm baths and gentle laxatives.

The medical soldier of Revolutionary days was not much more than an orderly, assigned for a day at a time to care for the sick. He was usually ignorant, untrained, undisciplined and anxious to be done with the miserable duty at the hospital. But this was true of all the wretched personnel who tended the wounded patriots. The straw-filled sacks on which the soldiers lay were issued in the same manner as clothing, and were supposed to be burned when the patients died.

Our country became free and independent, but in the years following the Revolution the soldier's plight was a sad one unless he miraculously escaped the ravages of disease, injury from accident, or wounds from tomahawk, arrow or gunshot. In 1811, troops quartered on the banks of the Mississippi near New Orleans suffered miserably from diseases of the swamps. Few provisions were made for their care, and there was no regular hospital detachment. There were no medicines, no organized hospital staff, not even an indifferent line soldier assigned to tend the sick as punishment for misbehavior. Food became rancid; beef and pork were so disgusting in odor that no one could eat them. Even as orders were issued to move to higher ground near Natchez, diarrhea, dysentery, high fever and scurvy broke out among the troops. There was no excuse for men to contract scurvy and suffer the ulcered gums, loosened teeth or even perforated cheeks caused by the disease; British Navy surgeon James Lind had years before proved the cure to be fresh fruits and vegetables (which as we know contain Vitamin C). Yet the soldiers did fall victim to scurvy, and they died for want of medical aid.

A year later, Dr. William Beaumont, famed Army physician who pioneered studies in gastroenterology, wrote of the plight of the wounded during one engagement with the British: "A most distressing scene ensues in the hospital—nothing but the groans of the wounded and agonies of the dying are to be heard. The surgeons wading in blood, cutting off arms, legs and trepanning heads to rescue their fellow creatures from untimely death. To hear the poor creatures crying, 'Oh, Dear! Oh, Dear! Oh, my God, my God! Do, Doctor, Doctor! Do cut off my leg, my arm, my head to relieve me from misery! I can't stand it! I can't live!' would have rent the heart of steel, and shocked the insensibility of the most hardened assassin and the cruelest savage. It awoke my liveliest sympathy and I cut and slashed for forty-eight hours without food or sleep."

Dr. Beaumont recommended a teepee-type field hospital for the care of the wounded, and it was during this period that Army medical men were given uniforms for the first time. It wasn't until 1851 that hospital stewards, the forerunners of today's Army medical men, were given a sleeve emblem: the caduceus embroidered in green. A little later it was adopted as a metallic cap ornament for stewards. It has been worn since 1902 to indicate membership in the Medical Corps. Dental, veterinary, medical service, sanitary corps officers and nurses wear it with the bronze letters D,V,MS,S, and N, respectively, superimposed.

During the Civil War soldiers on both sides were constantly stalked by disease: malaria, typhoid, typhus, "common continued fevers," smallpox, spurious vaccinia, scarlet fever, pneumonia, tuberculosis, catarrh and bronchitis. Common, too, were rheumatism, scurvy (because of dietary deficiencies) camp itch, venereal disease, alcoholism, mental depression, mania and dementia. It was a common sight in camps to see men's jaws tied up with bandages because of a mumps epidemic. There were many eye troubles and, as the war progressed, plain old ordinary malingering such as shooting oneself in the hand or foot in order to escape the front lines. Because of poor rations, bad cooking, impure water, fatigue and exposure, the Southern fighting men constantly fell prey to intestinal disorders of diarrhea and dysentery, and more soldiers were permanently disabled or lost to the service from these diseases than from gunshot wounds. Those afflicted seemed to lose their self-respect, their manliness, even their desire to live.

Both doctors in gray and doctors in blue worked courageously against overwhelming problems. Union and Confederate medical departments worked side by side, treating friend and foe alike. But the tasks were tremendous. In the Confederate Army, surgeon James Brown McCaw of Virginia headed the famous Chimborazo Hospital located on the hills in Richmond. It became one of the largest (9,000 beds) military hospitals that had ever existed in America. An independent community, with commissary service and other necessities, it consisted of 150 wooden buildings. Its own boats sailed along the James River to collect food. When the blockade cut them off from drugs and medical supplies, Dr. Francis Peyre Porcher, a botanist, collected medicinal plants that could be substituted for drugs.

In spite of such valiant efforts, 200,000 of the 600,000 mobilized Confederate soldiers died of wounds and disease. It is believed that only one-fourth died in battle; disease took the lives of the remaining 150,000. (In the Union Army there were 224,586 deaths from disease and 110,070 from battle.)

Assisting doctors in the Union hospitals were female nurses organized under Dorothea Dix, founder of this country's first insane asylums. These nurses were not trained; none such existed in the United States. They were volunteers who answered the call. Hundreds of women contributed their services, and although many administrative and disciplinary problems arose, they generally did a good job. The most noteworthy service by nurses was that of the Catholic nuns.

Male attendants were on a catch-as-catch-can basis and, as in previous wars, were not specialists. They were soldiers from nearby garrisons who were detailed to work in hospitals. The results were poor; no colonel wanted to lose a good man, even temporarily, so he grudgingly gave the hospital the worst he had. Usually the male attendants were convalescents, unfit for duty in the field. Many could not lift a patient, scour the floor, sit up nights or carry out beds. Frail, fretful and totally undependable, they had no feel for the job and made no effort to please.

It was obvious that something would have to be done; patients were becoming increasingly demoralized and enfeebled for lack of care. The only answer was to establish a regular

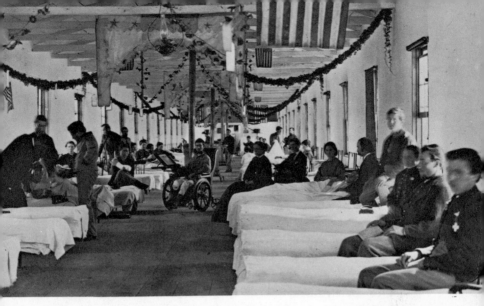

Female nurses assisted in Union hospitals during the Civil War. Shown here is Carver Hospital in Washington, D.C., decorated for the Christmas season. *U.S. Signal Corps Photo, National Archives*

Civil War surgeon Jonathan Letterman saw wounded wait for days before they could be evacuated to a hospital. *U.S. Signal Corps Photo (Brady Collection) in the National Archives*

enlisted hospital corps, with members specifically chosen for general hospital duty. In 1862 General William H. Hammond pointed out diplomatically that such a corps would allow several thousand detached men then serving in hospitals to return to their own regiments. He also mentioned that his new corps members could be chosen from men who had a tendency to hernia or who had poor eyesight. Nurses and cooks would continue to be civilians.

General Hammond's recommendations were approved, and the forerunner of today's hospital medical detachments was at last established. It was still not a hospital corps but at least the noncommissioned officers were permanently assigned to the Medical Department.

The new hospital stewards were given uniforms and held the rank of sergeant. For the first time they were screened for physical qualifications and were subject to military discipline. Appointees, it was hoped, were to be skilled in pharmacy and to possess such qualities as honesty, reliability, intelligence and temperance. It was their responsibility to see that the wards, kitchens, patients, attendants and articles in use were kept clean. The stewards also prepared provision returns, received and distributed rations and were the custodians of the hospital stores.

One of the most significant military medical achievements of the Civil War period, in which the medic played a prominent role, was in the evacuation of the wounded from the field of battle. When the war began, medical personnel were faced with what we would now consider an appalling and unbelievable situation. There was virtually no ambulance service between first-aid stations at the front and base hospitals in the rear. Theoretically there were two ambulances in the Army of the Potomac, but these were under the control of the quartermaster and could be used only temporarily during combat by the medical officer.

Assistant Surgeon Jonathan Letterman, Medical Director of the Union Army of the Potomac, took the first positive steps toward a system of removing sick and wounded soldiers from the front. He had seen men, wounded during the Battle of Bull Run, lie unattended for as long as a week and die in the open field for want of proper medical care. His plan, first used at the Battle of Antietam, employed field aid stations, ambulances, field hospitals, hospital trains and general hospitals. Officially adopted by the United States Army in 1864, it was standardized during the Spanish-American War. Litter bearers, a "chain of evacuation," carried the wounded from the front to aid stations, of which there were up to 800. Field ambulances then carried them to collecting or clearing stations. From there they were transferred to Army field hospitals for further treatment. The less seriously injured were returned to the front when cured; the others were sent to general hospitals for extended treatment and recuperation. This system is the basis for the modern techniques of evacuating the wounded.

The Civil War medic, the litter bearer and the ambulance attendant, though newly trained and not yet a part of an independent corps, nevertheless established a heroic heritage for their more professional counterparts of later years.

In the 1870's and '80's the Army medical soldier's life was one of adventure in the great West. His frontier-post hospital was a log building chinked with mortar, built in the shape of a parallelogram, with five rooms, a ward of twelve beds, an office, a dispensary, a kitchen and a storeroom. It was heated by wood-burning stoves, lighted by candles and ventilated by gaps in the chinking all around the windows. Water supply consisted of two or more pork barrels outside the kitchen, which, except in winter, were filled from an *acequia*, an artificial brook by which water was led to the post from higher up the river. In winter, the thermometer frequently reached minus forty-three and sometimes minus fifty-seven, at which times the snow or ice was melted on the kitchen stove.

With few exceptions, the hospital stewards proved to be excellent men. They tended the pharmacy, kept records, and managed hospital property and the wards. "Hospital Attendants" were also on the scene as private soldiers detailed to hospital duty. As in the past, these men were usually the worst the company commander had, because he didn't want to part with good personnel. History shows that the full-time hospital stewards were the real mainstays of the frontier Army hospital. These were the men whom doctors depended upon for devoted assistance in a wide variety of tasks, and whom officers and enlisted soldiers came to respect for the jobs they performed. Characteristic of the steward's assortment of chores was tooth extracting. The technique was quite simple—he simply shut his eyes, pulled, and listened for the crunch or snap of the crushed, broken molar or jawbone.

Hospital stewards rode with the cavalry into Indian country. Records indicate there was a medical soldier with General Custer at Little Big Horn. A few cavalry medics kept diaries of their experiences. One was Private H. Harbers, who gives a lively account of frontier life.

It was in the 1870's that his outfit headed into Indian territory, by way of Fort Dodge. There was no bridge across the Arkansas River, so the soldiers attached a rope to an empty water wagon and then sent it over. When the rope was taut, the men crossed the river hand over hand. They made camp, slept in the open and, when they got thirsty, marched fifteen miles to a good waterhole.

En route, they hunted game with their lone Springfield rifle to bolster their meager rations of hardtack and bacon. Since there were no vegetables, the men picked lamb's-quarters as greens and mixed them with wild garlic to ward off scurvy.

When the troops reached their destination, Private Harbers

proceeded to his barracks in the stockade. These boasted the usual dirt floors, and wood stoves for warmth. The bunks were wooden, double-decked affairs with straw mattresses. His uniform, which had been made by prisoners, didn't fit very well, but he didn't mind; no one else's did either.

The Indians "aroused the garrison" frequently by setting fire to the grass. Since all their water had to be drawn from a nearby creek, the soldiers beat out the fires with gunny sacks. During these frequent attacks by the Indians, Private Harbers usually found himself lying down behind the windows in the midst of cartridges strewn all over the floor. There simply weren't enough weapons and ammunition to go around, so he decided it would be wisest to lie low.

Now and then Private Harbers did minister aid to his comrades. He found a sergeant beneath a haystack with two arrows in his neck. The young private took him to the hospital where he "extracted the arrows," and his patient recovered nicely.

But all was not grim and brutal for the frontier medic. In July of 1874 his outfit received orders to exchange places with the 19th Infantry Station in the Department of the Gulf. In the true tradition of a military medic, Private Harbers called upon his powers of creative ingenuity to get the job done, in spite of all obstacles.

In his words, "Upon arrival at the west shore of the Arkansas river, a courier was awaiting the command. General Brooke, then a major, was in command of the three companies. The major called the troops to attention, but said not to get up as they were all tired out and then he spurted out the order that the paymaster would be in Fort Dodge tomorrow morning and to make an early start across the river which had to be done overhand as there were no bridges.

"We were all invited to a dance the evening of our arrival and I went over to see Mrs. Crowley, one of the laundresses of the company and asked if I could take Katy to the dance. She wanted to know how we were going to get there. I said, 'We will swim over.'

"I took both of our clothes and rolled them in a poncho to keep them from getting wet. We dressed in swimming togs by using Government drawers and shirts. We landed on the other side about three and a half miles below the Post. The water of the river is very swift. The girl was greeted by a bunch of women and wrapped in a blanket and carted off with the bunch of clothes to her room. I went to the barracks.

"The dance started promptly at eight o'clock and you would hardly have known that we both had swum the Arkansas river. The next day was payday and a hilarious time was had. The saloons and gambling houses were wide open and in Kelly and Beatty's saloon, the Officer of the Day came in and ordered the men to camp. One of the men full of liquor and beer, grabbed the Officer of the Day, took his belt off and threw him under the billiard table. . . ."

Fortunately there was no serious amount of bloodshed that day, and our hero apparently got Katy back across the river to her mother, the laundress, before everyone moved on.

In 1887, the Army Medical Department was at last formally organized. Men transfered from the line in the Army and became full-time, trained and authorized personnel, attached to the Medical Department as a corps. A few years later, in 1891, Colonel John Van Rensselaer Hoff organized the first company of instruction for the Hospital Corps at Fort Riley, Kansas, with a goal of developing the modern medical soldier. Hoff insisted that the medical soldier required as much training, including drill practice and field exercises, as did any other soldier, but that he should be trained in medical techniques as a "plus."

The Spanish-American War found the Army Medical Department desperately short of help. Though Congress in April 1898

July 1898. Spanish-American War casualties suffered from disease in crude hospital tents. *U.S. Signal Corps Photo in the National Archives*

Typhoid patient being taken to a hospital at Camp Meade, Pennsylvania. *U.S. Signal Corps Photo in the National Archives*

called for a volunteer army of 235,631 men, little provision was made for their medical care. To make matters worse, this enlarged army was to be sent into some of the most heavily disease infested areas of the world: Cuba, Puerto Rico and the Philippines.

Men riding, fighting and setting up camp in steaming swamps near polluted streams soon learned the hard way that one surgeon with two assistants and a handful of hospital stewards could never begin to care for an entire regiment at war on foreign soil. The entire Army had only 192 medical officers and 118 surgeons! The Medical Department needed 22,500, but only 6,000 were available. The grim statistics of the Spanish-American War are clear evidence that such meager help was indeed "pound foolish": 266 officers and men were killed outright in battle and 275 died of wounds, but deaths from disease reached the tragic total of 3,500.

In the past, some battles against disease had been fought by the Medical Department and had been won. Smallpox, for example, was challenged by Army surgeon Benjamin Waterhouse, who served in the War of 1812. It was he who brought to this country the vaccine from British surgeon Edward Jenner, and bravely vaccinated his own children, along with several servants. Seven persons in all submitted to his therapy and were then sent to a licensed smallpox hospital in Boston. None contracted the disease. It was through Dr. Waterhouse's efforts that the Army adopted the requirement of vaccination for all its members. Countless American lives were saved as troops marched into areas where the disease was as prevalant as prickly heat. Army medics played an important role in stamping out the disease among civilians when Colonel John Van Rensselaer Hoff received permission to vaccinate the entire Puerto Rican population. Armed with needles and vaccine and the knowledge of how to use them, medics fanned out to the provinces and went to work. By 1899, not a single case of smallpox

was reported. The problem in the Philippines was more difficult because of the greater population, the vast areas to be
covered and by the insurrection of the Hukbalahaps, who did
what they could to harass the Army Medical Department
workers.

Another scourge that stalked armies through the ages was
typhoid fever. During the Revolutionary War and Civil War,
typhoid and typhus, or "jail fever," were often confused with
dengue. It wasn't until 1862 that typhoid became the official
diagnosis. From then until June 30, 1866, there were 57,000
cases reported and 5,360 deaths. By 1898, the situation in military camps throughout the United States had got completely out
of hand, with some 20,000 men suffering the dread disease.
Nearly one-fifth of our soldiers contracted typhoid during this
period. Something had to be done to stop it, and soon.

Major Walter Reed headed a board set up for the control of
typhoid fever, and he and the other doctors showed that
typhoid was caused by food, fingers and flies. Although the
United States Army did not adopt compulsory prophylaxis
against typhoid until World War I, many procedures were
tested and tried for purifying water and sanitary facilities. Army
medics played a key role in amassing information and data.

As doctors and their enlisted assistants worked in the Philippines to control malaria, plague, cholera and dysentery, others
struggled to wipe out hookworm disease in Puerto Rico, studied
the causes of dengue fever and fought to control tuberculosis.
But much of the spotlight of those years was focused on yellow
fever, or "yellow jack."

This disease, which was probably carried to Cuba by colonial
troops when Havana was taken by the British in 1762, had long
been the enemy of the Army, but even more particularly of the
men who were trying to dig the Panama Canal. To appreciate its
lethal tracks, we have only to note that from 1881 to 1889 more
than 22,000 French laborers died of the disease. One station on

the old Panama railway was called Matachin, from the Spanish words *matar* (kill) and *chino* (Chinese) because 1,000 Chinese coolies died there in six months. Another 1,000 Negroes from the West Indies died during that same period. In Cuba, Puerto Rico and the Southern states there were some 1,164 cases in the Army, with 144 deaths.

The now-famed Yellow Fever Board was set up at Camp Lazear, Cuba, where an epidemic was raging. Headed by Major Walter Reed, the board set out to find the cause of the fever by using primarily their own individual deductions and observations. The studies began with a theory, stated in 1881 by the Scot-Cuban, Dr. Carlos Juan Finlay, that mosquitoes transmitted the disease. He based this theory on the fact that epidemics usually occurred in low, wet regions, while high and dry areas remained relatively free of the disease. Also he noted that the scourge spread in the direction of the prevailing wind.

The theory seemed sound enough to members of the board, but there were still skeptics who demanded proof before anything positive could be done about it. And the only way to prove the guilt of the mosquito was to call for human volunteers.

The first two men to come forward were hospital stewards.

Private John R. Kissinger was well aware of the risks involved. He had seen too many victims sicken and die, even as he tried to make them comfortable during their last hours. But if yellow jack was to be stamped out, the experiments had to be conducted. On November 20, 1900, in the sweltering hot tents of Camp Lazear, John Kissinger allowed himself to be bitten by three infected mosquitoes. Three days later, he was again bitten by the same three mosquitoes. On December 5 he exposed himself to five mosquitoes, two of which had been infected by *fatal* cases. On December 9 he became ill and suffered a typical case of yellow fever.

Private John Kissinger became the first case of experimental yellow fever in the series of tests at Camp Lazear. Major Walter

Reed later said of his hospital steward, "In my opinion, this exhibition of moral courage has never been surpassed in the annals of the Army of the United States."

Young Kissinger was discharged from the Army in 1901 "with character—excellent. . . ."

Private John J. Moran, hospital steward, an Irishman from the old country, had been working as a clerk at Department Headquarters when he became interested in the progress of the Yellow Fever Board. His admiration for Major Walter Reed was boundless, and when it came time for volunteers to prove the doctors' theories, he answered eagerly. He was bitten by infected mosquitoes on November 26 and again on November 29. Neither exposure produced results, but he was determined to keep trying. On December 21 he twice visited the infected-mosquito room. He returned the next day and was repeatedly bitten so that by Christmas Day, hospital steward John Moran had a full-blown case of yellow jack.

Moran refused to accept the bonus given to the volunteers by the government of Cuba. His reason was simply that he was glad to be able to do this service for humanity.

After his discharge from the Army, Moran headed for Panama, the "White Man's Grave," where he helped Major William Crawford Gorgas free the isthmus of the dread disease.

World War I had been in progress for two and a half years before the United States was drawn into the conflict. And this time was put to good use by the Army Medical Department. Through the cooperation of the Red Cross, Brigadier General Jefferson Randolph Kean organized fifty base hospitals at medical schools and hospitals throughout this country, and got them ready for service. At the time we entered the war the Army had a total of 131 station hospitals, four general hospitals and five temporary base hospitals. This was not being particularly generous because, before they were finished, the Army Medical

Ambulances carrying the wounded to Field Hospital Number 1, Neuilly, France, June 7, 1918. *U.S. Signal Corps Photo in the National Archives*

A 79th Division aid station in the Bois de Consenvoye, November 8, 1918. *U.S. Signal Corps Photo in the National Archives*

Department gave some 7,000,000 physical examinations and cared for about 4,000,000 sick and wounded doughboys.

In addition to the 833 physicians, 86 dentists, 62 veterinarians, 403 nurses and 6,619 enlisted medics at the war's beginning, the Army established an emergency "Sanitary Corps." These men were sanitary engineers, bacteriologists or preventive medicine experts, who were qualified to relieve medical officers of administrative duties and generally to eliminate disease hazards. As a result of this planning and foresight, World War I became the first conflict in history in which the number of deaths from disease fell below those in battle.

From the very beginning, the lifesaving noncombatants of World War I served with selfless courage and devotion, often at the risk of their lives. They were the first American military unit to reach Europe, and it was an Army enlisted medic, Private First Class Oscar C. Tugo from Boston, who became the first American to give his life in the "Great War." His death occurred before any line officers or men had been killed.

PFC Tugo, along with the others of his breed, carried no gun; yet the battle death rate for the medics was higher than in the aviation, cavalry, engineering, ordnance or quartermaster corps. Their sacrifice was exceeded only by that of the infantry, artillery, tank and signal corps. The reason for their vulnerability lay in their determination to stay close to the fighting man, an entirely new concept in the history of warfare. Their sole responsibility was to save lives and they were willing to do anything to accomplish that goal.

Killed in action, or died of wounds or disease;

    540 medical officers

    250 nurses

    2,257 medical soldiers

3

A Navy Hospital Corpsman with the Marines

WILLIAM Richard Charette, Hospital Corpsman
Second Class, serving with a Marine rifle company, was not yet
twenty-one years old on that early morning of March 27, 1953,
when he and the Marines with whom he served found themselves outnumbered and virtually trapped by North Korean and
supporting Chinese Communist divisions. Just four days before,
the Reds had taken the battle-scarred strategic position of Old
Baldy Mountain, and now they were determined to recapture
the South Korean capital of Seoul. Wave after wave of screaming Chinese attacked the leathernecks, trying to blast them out
of the chain of foxholes they had dug for themselves. Machine-
gun fire, mortar and artillery from cleverly concealed and well-
entrenched positions turned the battle into a raging inferno.

Suddenly from the forward trench came the calls for help.
"Doc! . . . Corpsman!" The young man from Michigan darted
out through the murderous hail of fire to answer the calls.
Repeatedly and unhesitatingly, he moved through the barrage

of hostile small-arms and mortar fire to render aid to his wounded comrades. With no regard for his own safety he applied tourniquets to badly bleeding limbs and injected morphine, hoping to ward off shock. It was while he was sprinkling sulpha powder into a gaping wound that he heard the dull thud a few feet away.

It was a grenade.

Instinctively he threw himself upon the stricken man he was attending. At that moment the enemy hand grenade exploded, filling the air with lethal fragments of torn metal. Charette absorbed the entire concussion of the deadly missile with his own body, and the Marine was spared further injury. But the young corpsman was bleeding from the painful wounds that peppered his face. His ten-pound medical aid kit had been torn from his body and his helmet blasted from his head.

Despite his own intense shock, he knew he must continue to act—and work—in his lifesaving role. His training would pay off at this critical moment. Those long hard hours of work at the Hospital Corps School in Bainbridge, Maryland, the book learning, lectures, demonstrations and exercises along with the practical experience at the Naval hospital in Charleston, South Carolina, would help him perform as he must. The rough field training he'd got from the Marines had taught him what to expect in combat. These Marines, "bell hops" or "gyrenes" as the Navy often called them, had accepted "swabbie" Charette as a part of their Marine family, and he wouldn't let them down now.

The numbness from the concussion began to wear off, and in that instant he quickly tore off part of his own clothing to improvise bandages. He administered aid to the wounded in his own unit and to those in adjacent platoon areas as well. Sometimes he crawled, other times he stumbled along in a crouched position. He was kneeling beside one wounded man as machine-gun fire chewed up the dirt and rocks nearby, when

Medal of Honor to William R. Charette, HM2, USN, presented by President Dwight D. Eisenhower, January 12, 1954. *U.S. Navy Photo*

he spotted a wounded Marine whose battle vest had been torn from his body by the blast from an exploding shell. Without thinking of his increased jeopardy, he removed his own jacket and covered the helpless man.

Moving to the side of another casualty who was suffering excruciating pain from a serious leg wound, Charette realized at once that the only way he could get at him and give medical aid was to expose himself. This he did without hesitation. Charette stood upright in the trench line for what seemed an eternity, an immobile target for the hail of enemy fire, so that he could better aid the victim and alleviate the man's anguish until he could be carried to safety.

It wasn't until the seriously wounded had been removed by stretcher from the battlefield that Charette allowed himself to be treated for his own painful wounds.

On January 12, 1954, at a White House ceremony, HM2 William Richard Charette was awarded the Medal of Honor "for conspicuous gallantry and intrepidity at the risk of his life above and beyond the call of duty.... By his indomitable courage and inspiring efforts in behalf of his wounded comrades, Charette was directly responsible for saving many lives. His great personal valor reflects the highest credit upon himself and enhances the finest traditions of the United States Naval Service."

Charette has been called a "miracle medic" because he lived through such fierce combat ordeals in the face of almost certain death. He continues to be a Navy Hospital Corps career man, making First Class in 1956 and teaching at the Hospital Corps School at Great Lakes, Illinois. After reenlisting he served at Jacksonville, Florida; Portsmouth, Virginia; and New London, Connecticut. He now serves aboard the submarine, U.S.S. *Quill-back*.

A solemn moment in the career of this Navy corpsman came in May 1958. Boarding the U.S.S. *Canberra* off the Virginia Capes, he placed a wreath on one of two unidentified caskets, thus choosing the Unknown of World War II to be buried in Arlington National Cemetery with the Unknowns of World War I and Korea.

4

They Began as Loblolly Boys . . .

THERE is a saying that used to make its way around
the old Navy wardrooms. It begins with a question: "Who is the
bravest man in the world?" to which the answer is, "The first
man who ever ate a raw oyster." The next question is, "Who is
the biggest fool in the world?" and the response to this one is,
"The first man who ever went to sea."

Undoubtedly this "world's biggest fool" was a primitive man
who tied logs together and made a raft to get from one side of
a river or lake to the other. His only serious hazards were alligators, poisonous fish or falling overboard and drowning.

As boats became large enough to be decked over and sail for
days or even weeks out of sight of land, new problems arose,
involving food supply, ventilation in crowded quarters and
care for the sick and injured. In the classical voyages described
by Homer, reference is made to the physician, or sanitation
officer, and from available evidence, the Greek fleet was excep-
tionally clean. Early Romans carried Immunes aboard ship.
These noncombatants held a status similar to that conferred on

modern noncombatants by the Geneva Convention of recent times.

During the Middle Ages, the only real contribution of nautical medicine came with the inspection and quarantine of ships returning from Asia Minor carrying cases of the Black Death. Even so, this plague killed over half the population of Europe.

Deep-sea navigation, beginning in the late fifteenth century with Columbus, Vasco da Gama and Magellan, introduced voyages that lasted for years; it also brought terrible scourges to sailors. Scurvy, typhus fever, smallpox and similar diseases relentlessly stalked every ship that set sail. Injuries, overcrowding, bad air and water supply, poor food and lack of care for the sick made a healthy existence for sailors virtually impossible. The number-one traditionally nautical killer was scurvy, a deficiency disease caused by a lack of Vitamin C in the diet. Without fresh fruits and vegetables, sailors after two weeks at sea would show signs of weakness, swelling of the legs and arms and softening of the gums so that teeth would fall out. Victims were prone to pneumonia and heart failure. Sir John Hawkins, the sixteenth-century naval captain, reported that in his twenty years at sea, scurvy killed 20,000 men in the British Navy. In 1522, the remnants of Magellan's historic voyage—eighteen survivors—completed the first circumnavigation of the globe. Most of those losses were from scurvy. On Lord Anson's military voyage in 1740, two-thirds of the crew died of the disease, 200 on flagship *Centurion* alone. By the time Cape Horn had been rounded and a few South Pacific islands reached, of the 961 sailors who began the voyage, only 335 were still alive.

Although preventive measures for scurvy had been known years before, it was not until 1747 that the British naval surgeon James Lind proved the value of lime juice in the treatment and prevention of the dread disease. Fifty years later, Sir Gilbert Blane was successful in making lime juice a requirement for all vessels of the Royal Navy; hence the nickname "Limeys" for the British seamen. This dramatic milestone in nautical medicine led to other improvements; in time, smallpox inoculation for the entire fleet was given official sanction.

The earliest clear record of surgeons and surgeons' mates in the Royal Navy is dated 1512 during the reign of Henry VIII. Reference is made to a commissioned officer who served as the ship's doctor. He had no regularly assigned assistant, but usually depended on a cabin boy, a cook or a convalescent to feed the sick and injured and to maintain cleanliness as best he could. Naval regulations stated that whenever a man was sick or injured, he was to be removed to the sick bay where he swung his hammock until his recovery.

Eventually, one of the ship's boys was assigned the task of assisting the surgeon and caring for the sick as a regular duty. He became known as a "waister" because the sick were located and treated at the "waist" of the ship, or as a "loblolly boy," because of the gruel or porridge he fed to the sick.

The duties of the loblolly boy are described in the United States Naval Regulations of 1814. "He will announce sick call in the morning by ringing the bell about the decks. He will feed, wash and shave the sick, and provide a tub of sand to catch the blood during surgical operations to prevent the staining of the deck. . . ."

The early loblolly boy's sick bay was an area set above the water line on the gun deck or berth deck, and was often exposed to enemy fire. It was soon discovered that a more sheltered area was needed for the wounded, particularly in the heat of battle. An additional space called the dressing station and operating room was set up in the cockpit. This area actually did double duty as living space for the midshipmen, surgeon's mates, master's mates, purser and the captain's clerk. Here, berths received the wounded and the mess table served as the operating table. Eventually, the sheltered cockpit, below the water line, was officially designated as "sick berth" or "sick bay" and was set aside for that purpose.

At the beginning of the Revolutionary War there were apparently no American Navy enlisted men trained in the care of the sick and injured. Certain of the least necessary or desirable crew members were assigned to assist the surgeon aboard ship.

It was June 1, 1778, that John Wall, recruited for the crew of the frigate *Constellation*, became the first man to enlist in the United States Navy as a full-fledged member of the medical department. In February of the following year, loblolly boy John Wall gained his first battle experience when sailors and marines defeated the French frigate *L'Insurgente* in a West Indies battle off the island of Nevis. The next month an act of Congress was passed regulating the medical establishments of the Army and the Navy. This act also provided for a "suitable number" of hospital mates to assist the surgeons. It is well that it did, for life aboard the early fighting ships was often a grisly, sanguinary affair. During an encounter with the enemy, boardings involved hand-to-hand combat with cutlasses, gun butts, clubs, chains or other hastily grabbed weapons. Cannon balls were heated red-hot before firing, and although they did not explode on impact, they caused many fractures of limbs. And the accepted treatment for compound fractures was amputation.

To prepare for such a booming business, loblolly boys turned to with such prebattle chores as providing the sick bay with water, locating containers for amputated limbs, arranging braziers of charcoal for heating the irons to sear the stumps caused by amputations, and heating the tar with which to stop hemorrhage. Loblolly boys also hustled about with the buckets of sand called for by the Naval Regulations.

Navy Regulations of 1814 specifically called for the loblolly boys to give patient care aboard ship, ". . . properly and carefully and with tenderness, discharging their duties faithfully and humanely . . ."

With the establishment of the Bureau of Medicine and Surgery in 1842, the term loblolly boy was changed to the more dignified surgeon's steward. His pay was listed as $18 a month and one ration. For the first time, surgeon's stewards were officially allowed at all hospitals and Navy yards, and on board every vessel that had a medical officer. Doctors were to select their stewards from men ". . . as have some knowledge of pharmacy and ordinary accounts and are of industrious and temperate habits . . ."

At the beginning of the Civil War, male nurses were accepted for duty aboard receiving ships. In 1866 the rating of surgeon's steward was replaced by that of apothecary in three grades. A caduceus worn on the uniform sleeve became the apothecary's emblem. By 1873 the surgeon's division consisted of junior med-

The U.S. Navy hospital ship *Red Rover* served during the Civil War. Photo: *U.S. Bureau of Ships in the National Archives*

ical officers of the ship, the apothecary and a newly designated "bayman," formerly called a male nurse.

It was a hard life then, particularly in time of war, for the lifesaving teams aboard ship. They worked in cramped, stuffy quarters with the rolling sea beneath them. Shortages of water, food and medicines were constant threats. Large modern naval vessels have medical facilities that are every bit as fine as can be found in any shorebound facility, but even today, small ships of older vintage are not so fortunate. Yet the crudest sick bay of today would seem a palace compared with those designed before the turn of the century.

For instance, there were no bunks, only hammocks in which the sick man could swing. If he were critically ill, he was bedded in a swinging canvas cot borrowed from the sailmaker.

There were no special facilities for surgery aboard vessels. Operations were performed in the sick bay on a wooden table, officially listed as a "combination writing and operating table," with a top hinged across the center. Most ships carried a fairly complete outfit of surgical instruments, which were sterilized by boiling in a special fish-length kettle heated by alcohol flame. The instruments were then placed in a tray and kept immersed in a five-percent phenol solution. Since there were no containers designed for sterilizing dressings, baymen and apothecaries kept a supply of empty twelve-pound coffee tins and six-pound sugar tins to use as containers for sterilizing gauze, cotton and other dressing materials. Sterilization by dry heat required the cooperation of the ship's cook, who looked after the coal fires in the galley; the oven was kept at a heat just under what would char the materials.

Fortunately, operations aboard ship in those days were fairly rare and the results generally good. The apothecary and bayman wiped down the operating area with a weak mercury solution if time permitted, and the operation began. It was a team effort all the way, with the surgeon doing the surgery, the apothecary assisting, and the bayman holding the sixteen-candle-power electric light to provide illumination without getting himself in the way of the surgeon.

During recuperation, the patient could rely on such faithful remedies as oakum soaked with oil of tar, iodoform on open wounds or Balsam of Peru with castor oil for ulcers. Baymen and apothecaries became highly skilled at applying dry and wet cups for a variety of ailments.

In caring for the sick, the early medical aidman had problems unique to his environment. For instance, fresh water was scarce and only the most modern ships carried a small water tank for special use in the sick bay. The precious fluid was doled out only for drinking purposes and for prescriptions. Sea water was used for all bathing and laundry.

Fresh provisions at sea were unknown, and because of the almost complete lack of cold-storage space on smaller or older ships, special diets came from canned foods or sometimes from the wardroom mess, which carried ice and fresh food for officers.

The early loblolly boy of John Wall's day had come a long way by the time he reached the ship's apothecary rating near the end of the nineteenth century. True, he'd had little instruction or training, but he carried his responsibilities with pride and honor. He ran the dispensary, compounded and dispensed medications and, since there were no typewriters on board ship, made out daily, monthly and quarterly reports in pen and ink. Baymen attended the sick, kept the dispensary storerooms clean, painted when necessary and sand-scrubbed the stools and benches. On "scrub bag and hammock days" baymen scrubbed the bags and hammocks belonging to those who were too ill to do their own. And always between times of tending the sick, there were paint-covered structures to scrape and salt-spray-dimmed metal to polish.

Unlike today's medics, whose job it often is to arrange the dead for burial, in the old fleet it was the sailmaker's task to sew a shipmate in his hammock for burial at sea. A pipe, tobacco and matches always went with the body in keeping with an old tradition of the sea. Old sailors swear to seeing the body going aloft the moment it was consigned to the sea.

It was during the Spanish-American War that the Hospital Corps was finally organized as a unit of the Medical Department under the provisions of an act of Congress, approved June 17, 1898. Twenty-five senior apothecaries of the Navy were appointed pharmacists. Dean of these men was an Irishman named Cornelius O'Leary, who had served thirty-seven and one-half years as an apothecary.

But a corps does not become distinguished simply because it is at last organized. The individual man is the final ingredient that makes the corps a great one.

Two years after the founding of the Hospital Corps, one of their own was awarded the Medal of Honor during the China Relief Expedition (Boxer Rebellion). The citation reads, "Standley, Robert, Hospital Apprentice, USN, in action with the relief expeditions of the Allied Forces in China during the battles of 13, 20, 21 and 22 June 1900. Throughout this period and in the presence of the enemy, Standley distinguished himself by meritorious conduct." Standley retired from the Navy on February 1, 1939, with the rank of Chief Pharmacist, after a long and colorful career. He died on July 15, 1942.

It wasn't until August 1902, 124 years after the first loblolly boy put to sea in a frigate, that a Hospital Corps school was established at Portsmouth Naval Hospital in Virginia. The oldest hospital in the Navy, it had been commissioned in 1830 and saw service during the crucial yellow fever epidemic of 1855 when, out of Portsmouth's 5,000 inhabitants, 1,000 died and another 1,000 were seriously crippled by the disease. The old thick-walled hospital with its massive Doric columns of free-stone served the Confederacy during the Civil War and as an important Naval hospital during the Spanish-American War. It was indeed a fitting place for the Navy enlisted aidmen to receive their first formal training in the care of sick and wounded. Graduates from this school experienced their first duty under fire with the Marines in Haiti, and later, during World War I, again with the marines, participated in the historic battles of Château-Thierry, Soissons, Saint-Mihiel and Belleau Wood to become the most highly decorated Navy unit of World War I. Here these young men, whose roots reached deep into their country's heritage, distinguished themselves not only as devoted workers but as professionally trained and qualified specialists.

John Henry Balch, Pharmacist's Mate First Class, served with the Sixth Regiment, U.S. Marines, in action at Vierzy. On July 19, 1918, Balch ". . . fearlessly exposed himself to terrific machine gun and high explosive fire to succor the wounded as they fell in the attack, leaving his dressing station voluntarily and keeping up the work all day and late into the night, unceasingly for sixteen hours on the field torn by shell and machine gun fire. Also in the action at Somme-Py on 5 October 1918 he exhibited exceptional bravery in establishing an advanced dressing station under heavy shellfire." So reads the Medal of Honor citation of John Henry Balch.

Two months after Pharmacist's Mate Balch's heroic action, a group of fellow corpsmen set out, unknowingly, to make history of a different sort. Somehow it didn't seem odd that the commanding officer of the Sixth Marines should order a chief pharmacist's mate and four other hospital corpsmen to set up an advanced aid station to care for casualties of the forthcoming battle. The corpsmen figured this was their job; it was what they had been trained to do. And so they started out through enemy-held territory, carrying aid kits but no guns. The trip took them from Thiaucourt, France, along the exposed left flank of the 89th Army Division, through the rattle of machine-gun fire and bursts of shells. Sometimes they ducked behind trees for cover or dove into holes as enemy fire harassed them. But at last they reached their destination, the town of Xammes.

Now, suddenly, all was quiet. Miraculously there was no opposition, only incredulous stares from the townspeople. But the corpsmen had no time for counting blessings, for there was work to be done. In short order, their advanced aid station was set up and ready for business.

Several hours later the wild-eyed assault force of the 89th Division cautiously moved into town to take possession. They were surprised, and not a little chagrined, to learn that the town of Xammes, their major objective, was already occupied by Navy hospital corpsmen.

Meanwhile, the battle continued to rage at Thiaucourt where David E. Hayden, Hospital Apprentice First Class, was caring for Marines of the Second Battalion, Sixth Regiment, who had been struck down by the enemy's fire. The crucial advance by the leathernecks had to be made, no matter what the cost in blood, and it was Hayden's job to save lives, even at the risk of his own. On September 15, 1918, Corporal Creed was among those gallant Marines who rushed across an open field, only to be hit by a vicious hail of machine-gun fire. The young corporal, mortally wounded, could not call for the corpsman, but Hayden saw him fall. That was enough. He grabbed his aid kit and ran into the storm of bullets and shells. Kneeling beside Corporal Creed, he saw at once that the only hope was to dress the wounds there and then, regardless of the perilous position. He went to work at once. And the Marines who witnessed the scene of a Navy corpsman disregarding his own safety as he tended one of their own, decided that Hayden was all right to have around. They later said it was a miracle that Hayden wasn't killed as he carried his wounded patient out of the fire-swept field to safety.

"For gallantry and intrepidy at the risk of his life above and beyond the call of duty . . . ," the citation reads. The Medal of Honor, destined to become almost a symbol of the medical soldier's, sailor's, or airman's role, was awarded David E. Hayden, Hospital Apprentice First Class, on behalf of a grateful nation.

5

Noncombatant Military Medics: A Special Breed

IT takes guts and valor for any man to go into battle. Even the professional soldier, sailor, marine or airman will feel the cold, dry horror of death's proximity. It is worse when reservists who have been called from their peacetime jobs on the farm, in the office or school are given a few weeks' basic training and sent into action. A man must be brave to pile out of a landing craft and storm a beach that is already red with blood from fallen comrades, to leap from a foxhole in the holocaust of bullets and mortar fire, bombings and explosions.

It requires nerves of steel for a sailor to speed through mine-filled waters, and to remain at his post in the haunting darkness of night. Beneath the seas' surface, a submarine hides on the murky bottom, its crew bracing themselves each time a depth charge threatens to blow them up. The airman in the skies must fly through flak-filled air over enemy territory, bombing and strafing strategic targets, knowing he is only seconds away from a flaming death. He bears this terrible burden bravely because

55

he knows he must, and because he has weapons with which to defend himself and to attack the enemy.

Great courage and fortitude are required for combat, yet the fighting man's mind is so occupied with the thought of defense and offense and his hands so busy with weapons, that his brain seldom has the opportunity to take stock of anything except the immediate objective.

The enlisted medical aidman of the Army, the hospital corpsman of the Navy and the aeromedical technician of the Air Force share all the anxieties of the fighting man, yet they are not killers but savers of lives. They have no screaming attack and battle on which to release these tensions; they have only the knowledge that their soothing, healing hands and words of encouragement have saved the lives of a lot of men.

It makes one wonder, because these noncombatants are tough customers when they have to be. They are not pale-handed orderlies who don't know how else to get out of their military service, or who are looking for an easy ride through life without having to fire a gun. They can't possibly be physically inferior to their fighting comrades because otherwise they couldn't keep up, they couldn't be with them when needed. When the infantry marches up the hill, so does the medic. When the infantry marches down the hill and continues for a forty-five-mile hike, so does the medic. If there is a group of more than five men going out on patrol (often less than five), a medic will be with them.

There are few places in this world, and certainly no specialized activity of the armed forces, where the medic is not deeply involved. Diving gangs, Underwater Demolition Teams and the top-secret SEAL (Sea, Air, Land) teams have their corpsmen, as do all ships of the fleet. Small ships, as well as certain submarines, have no doctors aboard and are completely dependent upon their highly trained corpsmen.

Because there could not possibly be enough doctors to staff

the thousands of isolated outposts, ships and planes, the medics are assigned such "independent duty" as substitute doctors.

When the airborne troops pour out of aircraft, their aidmen are sprinkled strategically throughout the force. There are medics with the Air Commandos of the Air Force and with the Rangers and Special Forces of the Army. When American military advisers (Military Assistance Advisory Group) were sent to Vietnam in 1954 following the Geneva Conference to help the South Vietnamese train for resisting aggression from the north, medics went along to look after their own men and to teach villagers basic hygiene and lifesaving techniques. Pararescuemen with Air Rescue Service parachute to the aid of downed airmen or survivors of just about any kind of disaster. When the Marines landed in Vietnam, so went their corpsmen, for whenever there is a buildup of fighting strength, the corpsmen are among the first considerations. These men, though cross-trained so that they can assume a wide variety of other vital jobs, must, as their main concern, "keep the fighting strength."

There are, of course, medics in all hospitals and dispensaries of the armed forces. Some help in the salvage of men's broken minds and bodies that are the perennial grim aftermath of war; others contribute to new techniques in research and practice. Some use their particular skills in dental technology or in the veterinary service. Many are engaged in sanitation and pest control. Others teach people of underdeveloped countries the benefits of modern hygiene, even to midwifery and everyday health habits. Even in peacetime there are casualties through accident and disease. Aeromedical technicians of the Air Force haul thousands of sick and injured military men, their dependents and many civilians in their airborne hospitals from areas all around the world to great hospital centers in the United States. Today in Vietnam, they are responsible for the aeromedical evacuation of wounded to hospitals where they can be properly cared for.

There are few natural disasters such as earthquake, fire and flood either at home or abroad in which medics will not be working around the clock giving first aid, doling out food, inoculating men, women and children, purifying water supplies and doing a myriad other tasks.

Sometimes the medic's job requires advanced technical skill and maturity far beyond his years; at other times his role is hard to define in a government MOS (Military Occupation Specialty) job description.

Take the boy whose jaw had been shot off by a sniper. He was all bandaged up, but the fluid from his salivary glands kept running down and choking him. He was loaded aboard an airevac plane along with a medic, who kept the G.I.'s head turned to one side and mopped his face. The boy couldn't talk; he couldn't even answer when the medic asked if he wanted anything. The G.I. reached up and brought the medic down to him. He didn't need anything. He just wanted someone to be near.

General Karl von Clausewitz wrote more than a hundred and fifty years ago: "War is the province of danger, and therefore courage above all things is the first quality of a warrior.

"There are however, two types of courage; physical and moral. Physical courage is exercised when in danger of death or injury; moral courage is a part of the execution of responsibility. Both may stem from pride, patriotism, enthusiasm or desperation. But both kinds are necessary to the fighting man."

The noncombatant military medic must also have a kind of inborn selflessness. He cannot give in to his natural instinct of self-preservation and survival when his own life is threatened, or men for whom he is responsible may die. Instead, he must consciously expose himself to death; he makes a perfect target as he hurries to the wounded man who cannot even crawl to safety. If a medic has to dash out to get a man, he likes to take a machine-gunner with him. He knows if he is shot by a sniper, the machine-gunner will at least avenge his death.

There was a time when an unarmed noncombatant whose job it was to take care of the sick and wounded could hope for respect and consideration from the enemy. At the Geneva Red Cross Convention of 1864, representatives from many nations agreed that attacks on such men were uncivilized and immoral. Hospitals, ambulances, doctors, nurses and medics should be spared from attack. On March 1, 1882, during the Garfield Administration, the United States became a signatory of the pact, and within a short time fifteen other nations had signed. A flag with a red cross on a field of white was adopted as an identifying marker by all countries agreeing to the pact, and it was to be prominently displayed at all medical facilities and on vehicles used for humanitarian purposes. Aidmen, corpsmen, litter bearers and, of course, doctors and nurses were to wear the symbol on an identifying armband and on helmets.

The familiar Red Cross flag is actually the reverse of Switzerland's flag, which is a white cross on a red field, and it was chosen as a tribute to the city in which the convention was held. The origin of the symbol dates back more than 800 years before the convention to the crusading Knights of St. John of Jerusalem, who dedicated their lives to caring for the sick and injured of the Crusades.

The Red Cross insignia was first worn by American medics in 1887 when Congress passed the law authorizing a Medical Department for the Army. Men transferred from the line and became known officially as hospital stewards. In 1898, the Navy purchased the S.S. *Creole* and converted her into a hospital ship, the U.S.S. *Solace*. A group of male nurses recruited from Bellevue Hospital in New York served as hospital attendants with the bizarre rating of "ship's cook (nurse)" and were each given a Geneva Cross armband. The U.S.S. *Solace* flew the Geneva Cross flag.

Soon after the purchase of the U.S.S. *Solace*, on June 17, 1898, Congress passed the act which created the Hospital Corps of the Navy. The "ship's cooks (nurses)" were put into uniform with the Geneva Crosses on their sleeves.

During World War I in Europe the Red Cross designation was generally respected, and there are only a few reported instances when it was deliberately fired upon. During World War II, the Germans seldom set out to kill medics and destroy aid stations. In fact there was often a strange camaraderie between medics of opposing forces as they found themselves helping one another's patients.

In the Pacific, it was a different enemy and a very different kind of war. Early in the Guadalcanal campaign, Navy corpsmen serving with the Marines learned that the Japanese had never been signatories of the Geneva agreement and that the Red Cross marking meant nothing to them except a target. Snipers deliberately tried to pick them off, not because they were killers but because they saved lives. A corpsman was a real trophy because that meant a lot of Marines were put out of action. It was definitely not a gentleman's war.

On Guadalcanal, corpsmen stripped off their Geneva Cross brassards, painted over the markings on their helmets and smeared mud on their ambulance jeeps to cover the cross. For the first time, they armed themselves with .45s and sometimes carbines for self-protection and for the protection of the patients. Since that campaign, to this day Navy hospital corpsmen wear no distinctive Red Cross insignia. Shortly after the start of operations in Korea, Army medics likewise removed the Red Cross markings from themselves, their equipment and aid stations.

Life for the noncombatant medic on the field of battle is far from safe. During World War II, 3,061 Army medics were killed in action; 1,724 Navy hospital corpsmen died as snipers' bullets pierced their mud- and blood-soaked uniforms and shattered the plasma bottles they held over their patients who lay bleeding in the sand. In at least one campaign—Iwo Jima—the mortality rate among hospital corpsmen was higher than that among the fighting troops. This was because the corpsman could never let up, especially when the fighting was that heavy.

Medics don't want to die, but they do die because they believe their cause is larger than merely surviving. Perhaps that is what makes death more bearable.

In a way it could be said that the nation's highest award, the Medal of Honor, typifies the spirit of all the medics in the armed forces. The medal itself signifies the unusual—the man who performs above and beyond the call of duty. Considering the fact that the medics represent only a minute fraction of the overall military strength, their awards for courage and bravery are revealing for their disproportion. As an example, all seven Medals of Honor awarded the Navy Medical Department during World War II went to enlisted hospital corpsmen serving with the Marines at either Okinawa or Iwo Jima. Also during World War II, 67 Navy Crosses and 464 Silver Stars were awarded Navy corpsmen. During the Korean conflict, five out of seven Medals of Honor awarded the *entire Navy* were given to noncombatant sailors of the Hospital Corps.

Almost every decoration for which they are eligible has been awarded in large numbers to the medics; this includes many foreign decorations. Hospital corpsmen who served with the Marine Corps in France during World War I are the only Navy men privileged to wear the French Fourragère. In 1946, Secretary of the Navy James Forrestal gave a blanket commendation for the heroic work of the Hospital Corps during peace and war. It is the only time in the history of the Navy that a single corps has been so honored.

The medics are justifiably proud of their heritage and the honors that through the years have been heaped upon them. Yet the real thing that keeps them going is the G.I., the sailor, the Marine or airman. Their appreciation tumbles out, often in a disjointed, spontaneous way, but it makes sense.

"Don't take our word for it. Just go to the Ninth or Thirty-fourth and ask any G.I. you meet on the road. Last week a lot of guys passed out from the heat, and then the Koreans drove us back. The Koreans bayonet anybody they see on the ground— just to make sure they're dead. Our medics went forward after we had retreated and pulled back the guys who were still alive. One of the medics got it right through the head, but the other one got everyone back okay. . . ."

Another thing that keeps the medic going is the knowledge that nowadays, compared with the past, he can do so much good for his men. He knows that with antibiotics, whole blood, modern surgery techniques and aeromedical evacuation by fast airplanes, he can save more men from death than ever before in history. During World War II, 98 out of every 100 men the medics patched up in the field of combat and got to aid stations and hospitals, recovered. The disease rate was only one-twentieth as high as in World War I. During the Korean War, 99.4 out of every 100 wounded men recovered. Today, military medicine has raised that figure for surviving wounded even higher.

In today's cold-hot wars the logistics of the medics varies with military buildups and cutbacks, but their number is relatively small—too small. In combat, there are never enough to go around, and that is why each individual medic must call on every ounce of strength he has. Today's Army has about 44,000 medics actively engaged in patient care in hospitals and in the field. The strength of the Navy Hospital Corps is about 24,800, with some one-third of the corpsmen on duty in Naval hospitals and the remaining two-thirds attached to fleets, the Marine Corps and units of the shore establishments. There are about 25,000 aeromedical technicians currently serving in Air Force hospitals, dispensaries, air-evac planes, laboratories and units in the field.

Who are they? What are they? Where do they come from?

There are no simple answers, except to say they represent a cross section of American life. Sometimes they are civilians who turned to the military when their country needed them. Other medics are draftees living up to a solemn obligation. To many who are "regulars," the military is their way of life. They come from all states in the Union and from homes that are rich or poor. For many medics from deprived homes, the training and experience they have in the military prepares them for a wide variety of skilled jobs in civilian life. An appreciable number of medics go to medical schools after their enlistment is up and become doctors. The demand for a military medic in civilian hospitals, pharmacies, sanitation and health departments, drug companies and research corporations is always greater than the supply. It is remarkable that so many of them remain in the military at a fraction of the pay they could get on the "outside."

Some enlistees specifically ask for training and duty with the medics because they have always been interested in "medical things," but others are simply assigned to that category because the need for them exists and because the new man shows aptitude and ability in his tests. On the whole, medics have superior motivation and intelligence; otherwise they could not cope with the specialized training they must have.

The age of the new medic varies, but often he is a very young man—a boy—who perhaps lies about his age of sixteen or seventeen in order to enlist immediately after high school. He goes through basic training, the same as any other enlistee. From there he usually goes to one of the specialty schools.

The medic may seem to be very much like his contemporaries in mannerisms and appearance, but there is a special maturity about him that develops very early in his military career. Undoubtedly it is the result of the responsibility for others' lives and safety that rests on his young shoulders. That responsibility can be an awesome one for a lad of, say, eighteen years of age

who has never before left his home town. Suddenly his decisions, his actions mean life or death to officers and men, women
and children in areas of the globe whose names he can scarcely
pronounce. He sometimes thinks of the life he has just left—his
contemporaries hot-rodding around town or going to football
games or playing records at the malt shop—and he can hardly
believe he could change so much so fast.

Medics, corpsmen and med techs often work together, side
by side in different uniforms, but with the same common goal—
saving lives and alleviating pain. In each of the services, these
enlisted men are considered a part of the Medical Department
team, which includes the physicians, nurses, dentists, veterinarians and Medical Service Corps (MSC) officers. There are also
many female trained medics in all three branches of the service, and except for combat duty, they perform somewhat the
same tasks as the men. In addition, there were the colorful
canine warriors who were trained during World War II to crawl
forward to the aid of isolated personnel.

No disrespect or lack of appreciation is intended by confin-
ing this story to that of the enlisted male medic of the Army,
Navy and Air Force. Neither is it an attempt to "simplify" a
story of thousands upon thousands of men, who through the
years have served unselfishly in the highest calling—the saving
of life—both on the firing line and in the ceaseless war against
disease and premature death. Rather it is an attempt to bring
out some of the highlights in the history and career of a special
breed of men—the noncombatant military medic.

Official designations and nicknames for these men have
changed many times through the years. And what appears on
paper as the official rating does not mean that this is the name
they go by. For instance, men needing help on the battlefield
do not call out "Medical Technician!" or "Aidman" or any of
the other "paper" titles; they call "Medic!" if they are in the
Army. In the Navy or Marine Corps, they call "Corpsman!"

rather than "Pharmacist's Mate" or "Specialist Something-or-other." In the Air Force, the cry is "Med Tech."

Because of this somewhat confusing nomenclature, I use the favored "non-paper" terms as often as possible: medic, corpsman and med tech. This seems appropriate because it is the way their men think of them.

6

World War II — in Europe

T two o'clock in the morning of June 6, 1944, Sergeant Charles F. Short, a medic attached to the 507th Parachute Infantry Regiment, prepared to jump into the night sky over enemy-held France. The timing, though hazardous, was logical. Darkness would give the paratroopers some protection from enemy fire, but more important, the Allies would plant key men behind German lines hours before the invasion of the Normandy coast. Their mission was to disrupt German communication lines, and generally to raise havoc whenever possible and eventually link up with the invasion forces, which would come at dawn.

Sergeant Short checked his medical equipment with care and what he hoped was foresight. There would be no replenishing of supplies once he stepped out of the airplane. He tightened the straps that fastened the two aid kits to his legs. Wire ladder splints and basswood splints were in canvas pockets, also strapped to his legs. In his kits were morphine syrettes to deaden pain and ward off shock and containers of sulpha for sprinkling into open wounds. Bandages, scissors, disinfectants and plasma along with an assortment of pills and antibiotics weighted him down so that he lumbered about the noisy plane like an outerworld creature. Unlike his comrades, who resembled lethal arsenals, Short carried no weapon at all. He hoped the Germans would respect the Red Cross markings on his sleeve and helmet.

The plane had approached the narrow peninsula of Normandy from the northwest, and now, ten minutes after it crossed the shoreline, the Germans spotted it. Tremendous barrages of antiaircraft fire burst all around the low-flying airborne troopers. Stuff was even coming through the floor of the plane. And this was what men were supposed to jump into!

Finally word was passed down the line. "Captain Ray says it would be suicide to go out here. We'd better wait a couple of minutes till we get away from the worst of it."

Two minutes. That meant when they did jump they would be spread out all over a countryside the terrain of which they had not studied on their sandtables. Two minutes. Scarcely enough time for Short to think back on how he became an airborne medic.

He was twenty-four years old at the time he enlisted in the Army in January 1942, and after taking his basic training at Fort Lee, Virginia, he and four of his buddies volunteered for airborne school at Fort Benning, Georgia. He got through it all right, even though he never got to like parachuting as some did. And then Short decided to become a medic because accidents did happen in training; in combat, his medical services would be even more vitally needed.

After a two-month course in basic medical treatment and hospital work at the medical technicians training school at Lawson, Alabama, he returned to the tarpaper shacks at Fort Benning and served in a medical detachment there.

The war was moving ahead fast and the 82d Airborne Division was rarin' to go overseas to show the stuff of which they were made. Even as Short's regiment moved to Nebraska for a short time prior to shipping out to Ireland, every man kept up his physical conditioning at a feverish pitch. There were push-ups, runs and marches, and when airplanes weren't available for training jumps, the men kept in trim by rolling out of a moving two-and-a-half-ton truck. "Airborne all the way" meant just that, and now Short was glad these men had the spirit and tough conditioning for the harrowing jump they were about to make.

There were other airborne aidmen. Some sixty of them were headed for Normandy one way or another, and he dimly wondered how they would fare in next few hours. In his own medical detachment there were four doctors. There was also a dentist, whose job it was to repair facial injuries, perform emergency extractions and serve as aidman. Everyone was airborne, including the chaplain, who, when not performing holy rites, would also act as aidman. Short remembered the Holy Joe's way of saying, "Where do you want me, Charlie?" as he laid aside his Bible.

Now as the roar of the engines droned in his ears, Short saw the jumpmaster signal *one minute*! The men were at the open door waiting for the red light to change to green and chanting "Go! Go! Go!" as they whipped up their enthusiasm. The light turned green, and they were away, swinging into the chilling black windstream of night two seconds apart. Interspersed among the silent figures swaying beneath the nylon mushrooms were the men without guns—the medics.*

Sergeant Charles Short was one of thousands of combat medics spread all over the globe during World War II. Wherever the fighting man was in need of medical aid—in Africa, Europe, Asia, the South Pacific, Alaska, Australia—the enlisted lifesaving specialists were close at hand.

* From an interview with the author.

These medics were not the untrained misfits, the feeble convalescents of historical wars, but highly motivated, educated, physically qualified military personnel. Usually they were a cut above average intelligence with a proven aptitude for science and medical matters. And they weren't just a token handful of men whose job it was to care for the high-ranking officers, but a massive force designed to keep as many men at as many guns for as long a time as was humanly possible.

This force included physicians, dentists, nurses, veterinarians, medical administrators, sanitation experts, pharmacists, dieticians, physical therapists, medics—the entire spectrum of modern health and lifesaving specialists. And the force burgeoned with the same desperate speed as did the all-out mobilization. As an example in 1939, the total strength of the Army Medical Department was 2,181. In 1940, that figure was roughly doubled. By D-Day in June of 1944, the total force of the AMD was 673,316 men and women. Of this figure, 553,095 men were Army enlisted medics. There were 137,000 enlisted hospital corpsmen in the Navy.

Because of the national emergency, many of these combat medics had little time for formal training before heading for overseas battlefields. This was especially true of Army medics, who served where doctors and nurses were on hand to teach them, on the job. But even without much formal classroom work, the selflessness and empathy of those new recruits soon carved a permanent niche of gratitude in the hearts of the G.I.s they tended. Litter bearers, ambulance drivers and hospital-equipment maintenance men all learned to double in brass in patient care. Often they were not specialists but simply Army aidmen with a compassion for others, and were as much a part of the medical team as the most highly specialized physician. Their Medals of Honor and other awards prove this point.

It is generally recognized that the Navy corpsman has been consistently well trained in a formal manner, even in wartime, before being assigned anywhere in the United States, with the fleet or with units of the Marine Corps. This is necessary because the Navy corpsman is so often on "independent duty," that is, where no doctor is available. A raw, untrained recruit could not learn on the job, because too many decisions are life-and-death ones.

Hundreds of thousands of G.I.s who fought in Europe remember the medical teams and the tented hospitals that were hastily erected like giant Ringling Brothers show palaces. Usually they can't remember the name, but they recall the fatigue-lined face of the doctor who sutured up the gaping wound, the nurse whose inner calm and efficient manner allayed a lot of fears, and the medic who scurried about, doing just about anything that needed doing. Conversely, the medical team members seldom remembered the soldier's name, but they remembered his case. What a nightmare it was to pull him through. Or did they? Did the patient expire later? They seldom knew.

The wounded warrior was treated far differently from those in past conflicts. If he were not killed outright or wounded so badly that nothing could save him, he had every right to expect that he would live. For one thing, there were the advances of medicine itself: improved surgical techniques and the use of sulpha drugs and penicillin. The latter two reduced the pneumonia death rate from twenty-four percent in World War I to six percent in World War II. The use of blood plasma, atabrine for malaria, DDT powder and spray for control of malarial mosquitoes and typhus lice saved millions of lives, particularly in Italy, the Balkans and the Pacific.

And then there was the "chain of evacuation" so dear to the heart of Civil War surgeon Jonathan Letterman. During World War II the system, which looked so good in theory and on paper, was also amazingly effective in the field of combat. It began with a wounded soldier giving himself first aid, if possible, from his personal kit. He also had sulpha tablets for swallowing and a small sack of sulpha powder for sprinkling on his wounds, if help were delayed in reaching him. He then tried to make his way back to the battalion aid station, which was usually a few hundred yards from the front line. If he were hurt so badly he could not take care of himself, the medics rushed out to help him. They gave him sulpha or morphine, dressed his wounds to prevent hemorrhage, applied splints for fractures, made tourniquets and gave plasma when indicated. If the medics needed to move on with the advancing troops, they attracted the attention of litter bearers, who carried the G.I. back to the battalion aid station. From there he was moved by ambulance to the clearing station, where he was "classified" as to the extent of his wounds or illness. If he were seriously injured or needed surgery, he was sent on to the field hospital. Patients who were not likely to recover within, say, thirty days or who were permanently disabled were moved to an embarkation hospital, where they awaited transportation by hospital ship or plane back to major hospital centers in the States. Of course, anyone involved with this theoretical picture of how things were supposed to work will hasten to explain that variations were the rule rather than the exception. Men come to expect just about anything in time of war.

The Army medic in Europe lived with every possible extreme, from the violence of the front to the hushed, teetering, life-death precipice of the field-hospital shock ward. In Oran, he worked in one of five big Army hospitals, four of which had been taken over from the French and the other, a huge tented establishment, set up in an oat field. He became a desert nomad as his hospital was knocked down and moved along behind the battling troops, only to be set up again in a matter of hours, or at the most a couple of days. He dug ditches, unloaded truckloads of medical supplies, drove tent pegs and tapped local power lines for electricity. Along with the doctors and nurses he painted signs, laid canvas on the ground as floors, tacked mosquito nets over cots and, when patients began to arrive, framed pictures of the G.I.s' wives and children.

Mornings, they got up before daylight and bathed out of helmets. They were allowed one quart of water each day for bathing and laundry.

Medics worked in the surgical and laboratory tents, both of which had the finest, newest equipment available anywhere. Often it was their job to see that the triple flap was pulled over the surgical tent entrance and the heavy mosquito bar was properly dropped over it. Sometimes they worried about the problems of electrical current, but once the hospital was hooked up to nearby high-tension wires, operations proceeded fully, even fiercely, illuminated. Medics assisting in the OR, when the entrance flaps were down, learned to work and survive in the almost unbearable heat.

They worked in the X-ray room with its fluroscope—a darkroom that was a tent within a tent—and they brought patients up the muddy streets on stretchers that ran on bicycle wheels. They worked in the dental office, which was at one end of the surgical tent, and they tended the drugstore where thousands of prescriptions were filled in endless bottles. Pot-bellied stoves kept them warm during the long, cold winter nights. That is, when they were ingenious enough to "moonlight requisition" the necessary firewood.

Patients came from all over. Even wandering Arabs who had picked up a war injury stopped by the Oran hospital for treatment. By December 1943, hospital ships like the *Algonquin* were bringing them casualties from Bizerte, North Africa, and later from Sicily, Naples and southern France.

Medics served long, hard hours aboard these ships. PFC James Loveall (now Sergeant First Class) was only nineteen years old at the time he found himself wearing the badge of a combat medic and sailing through the Mediterranean with a shipload of combat casualties. This was a long way away from that Oklahoma farm he'd left at the age of sixteen to join the CCC. And it was a far cry from Camp Barkley, Texas, where he'd trained for sixteen weeks to become a combat aidman in the Army. In an all-out war, sea duty was not just for bell-bottom-trousered sailors of the Navy.

Army hospital ships in the "Med" were painted white, were fully illuminated day and night and displayed huge Red Crosses on their smokestacks and sides. Medics aboard them knew they were under constant surveillance by enemy submarines and air-craft, and they were aware of the fact that, as a perfect target, they could be blown out of the water at any time. One hospital ship did go down in that manner.

But these floating hospitals had to follow the Allied invasion forces regardless of the risks. Men ashore were fighting and dying, and the medical teams would not let them down.

And so they came, hour after hour . . . the battered, torn war-riors of the invasions. They arrived in little boats or barges or whatever craft was available for their transportation to the mercy vessel. Using block and tackle, human muscle and often strong language, medics got the litter baskets aboard, but it was always a slow, painful procedure. The wounded, who had been given first aid at the front, were checked again aboard ship and bedded down in emergency, surgery, or whatever clinic or ward their condition called for. During the heavy fighting, the wards became full to overflowing. These are the times Loveall remembers lining up cots side by side on the decks to take care of more, and more . . . and still more.

There came a time when there was no room left in the field hospitals overseas. Hospital ships had no choice but to make the long voyage back to the United States with their loads of wounded men. Loveall made sixteen such trips during his five months aboard the *Algonquin*. And in that same five months, he spent exactly six hours ashore. He had no leave, no break at all from what amounted to almost a twenty-four-hour-day service.

"But," he explains, "I wouldn't have left if I could. There was too much to do. Too many guys . . . you know?"*

As hospital ships loaded their wounded and carried them to safety, combat medics with the invasion forces spread themselves among the troops to give help wherever needed. You never knew where you'd find them, but they were always a mighty welcome sight.

During the invasion of Sicily in July 1943, John Moroso, a correspondent with the Associated Press, remembers his swim ashore through a predawn, stormswept sea. His landing craft had been wrecked, and it was every man for himself, getting to land as best he could. Suddenly he heard a call for aid from the nearby water. It was an American lieutenant who was drifting helplessly in the waves because his leg had been terribly shattered as he was leaving his landing craft.

Moroso towed the injured officer up onto the beachhead. Then, in violation of orders forbidding any shouting by the invading forces, the correspondent yelled into the dark, "Medic! Medic!"

Immediately not one but two medics materialized from the inky blackness and took charge. The beachhead was being swept by enemy fire and the ocean spray was pouring over them, but they went on with their work. Proceeding without lights, since it was strictly forbidden to show any, they set the lieutenant's leg and put splints on it. All this was done by sense of touch, with an expertness acquired from being trained to work in the dark. Then they got their man into a small boat which took him to the assault transport *Thomas Jefferson*. A doctor there said the leg couldn't have been set better aboard the ship.

Some of the hardest workers, all of whom were volunteers, were the litter bearers. These men could not defend themselves

* From an interview with the author.

Captain John L. Strader, Commanding Officer, 35th Infantry Division, is shown being removed by medics from the St.-Lô, France, front to a field station where his leg wounds will be treated. July 21, 1944. *U.S. Army Photograph*

at all. They could not dodge bullets or duck into foxholes; they could not even run because they were carrying a wounded man on a stretcher. They worked in complete blackout near the front lines where cigarettes, flashlights or matches were forbidden. It was a hard job putting a tag on a wounded man, and often the litter bearer had to dig a hole and get a blanket under which he could use a light—or he would simply write it out in the dark. Every wounded man had to be tagged so that medical personnel up the line would know what medications had already been given.

In mountainous regions, mules wouldn't work on precipitous slopes in the dark, so the job fell to the medics. If the terrain were bad enough, one stretcher might have to be transported by as many as eight men: four carrying the stretcher, one lugging everyone's aid kits, two in front to clear the way and hold back the scrub brush so that the stretcher could pass, and another acting as a relief. Ideally the patient would be kept at a level position as he was lowered over sheer banks, hauled across ravines and gently eased around the narrow mountain trails. So the medics skidded and slid, propped poles on their shoulders or carried them at an almost completely bent-over position.

Litter bearers and aidmen sometimes got to come back from the front line to the collecting station for a bit of rest and quiet. It was like the Grand Hotel as they curled up in their foxholes and slept. When they were awakened and told that it was time to go up to the battalion aid station again, they hopped in their jeeps and took off.

Meanwhile, in England, medics were sweating out the return of aircraft that limped back through flak-filled clouds after dumping their bombs on strategic targets. Usually the planes came back late in the day through the heavy weather that hangs over Britain. The doctors and medics stood by with their ambulances, waiting for the signal from the planes that there were wounded aboard. If flares were dropped, the ambulances would race down the field and screech to a stop. Doors were flung open, medics jumped out, grabbed their litters and headed for the aircraft. At most of the English air bases, medical facilities were housed in little Niessen huts. Pot-bellied stoves kept the patients warm.

As the fighting continued, medics learned that the standard equipment furnished them was adequate for the classroom but not for the battlefield. Since it was too late to argue about it, they improvised their own gear. Medics knocked out the rear seats of jeeps and converted them into litter carriers. It didn't matter if parts of the litters hung over the back as long as the job got done.

They discovered that hanging a plasma bottle on a rifle that was stuck into the ground provided the needed gravity for the fluid's flow, while it freed both hands for first-aid work. The same principle worked at aid stations, where medics wrapped plasma bottles in gauze and attached them to the inside of the tent with a safety pin.

Sergeant Major John R. Hatten (who is now at the Ninth Hospital Center in Heidelberg, Germany) recalls some of the departures from the "Carlisle Solution." Carlisle Barracks is where he had been trained.

"Bandaging a sucking chest wound is always a problem because the gauze will stick to the skin. When we arrived in England before the D-day invasion, we learned that the Allies had captured some vaseline gauze from the Germans. This was great stuff, but we had none of our own—so we made some. Then we ran around collecting cookie cans from G.I.s who'd received treats from home. These we sterilized and put the home-made vaseline gauze inside. Properly sealed, the system worked just fine."*

On the Normandy beachhead during blackouts, surgery tents had the problem of getting sufficient light inside the heavy flap curtains. Double portable dynamos were used, but often the necessary illumination came from flashlights. To increase the brightness, medics rigged up reflectors which they fashioned from empty blood-plasma tins.

D-day. June 6, 1944.

Sergeant Charles Short, parachuting into the darkness over France, drifted down, down, down under an inflated canopy he could not see. Hips relaxed, knees together—he remembered he was not to look down. He fervently hoped for a good PLF (parachute landing fall) because even a minor injury in enemy-

---

* From an interview with the author.

held territory could be fatal. With no weapon at all, he was completely at the mercy of any Nazi who might find him.

He landed in a ditch of some sort and immediately cut himself out of his chute. And then he waited for what seemed an eternity, but the luminous dials on his watch told him it was only a half hour. The stillness of the dark night was frightening, but suddenly he heard noises of movement through the grass a few feet away. He cautiously crept out of his ditch only to discover a cow peacefully grazing in the pasture.

Somewhat sheepishly, he began his cautious journey down the narrow dirt road. And then he saw the outline of what he *knew* was a man. Was it friend—or foe? The only way to find out was to challenge the man with the prearranged code word.

"Mona!"

He held his breath, waiting for the hail of bullets or the relief of a proper reply. The word came quickly.

"Football!"

It was another medic. Now things began to look pretty good again as the two men decided what they would do next. "The Five-oh-two Regiment has got to be in the vicinity. We'll find 'em." Before long, Sergeant Short had lined up twelve paratroopers and, since he was now the ranking man, decided they would head for Ste.-Mère-Eglise . . .

Dawn on the Normandy coast, and the beginning of the largest amphibious landing in history. Hundreds of ships anchored in a gigantic circle, their darkened hulls defined against the slowly lightening water. Scores of small boats splashed from ship to shore and back to ship again in frenzied activity. Men clambered up and down ladders and nets, dropped into heaving boats, leaned far over the rails to shout hoarsely into megaphones or stood, like those on the transports, and waited. Far out to sea, the destroyers and corvettes, their sirens bleating feverishly, wheeled and circled, guarding the dangerous outskirts of their flocks. The Allied armada of 4,000 ships had arrived.

Medical plans were that the care of casualities from enemy action during the invasion was to be an Army commitment. The Navy was to take care of men who were injured in loading accidents or near-shore enemy action. The Army was supposed to turn over to the Navy any naval casualties returned from the far shore and any patients who were in poor condition on arrival at a near-shore unloading point.

By cold calculation, strategists estimated that 17 out of every 100 men of the landing force would become casualties. It was decided that all "ineffectives" except nontransportables should

D-Day.
American medics of the 8th Infantry Regiment, 4th Infantry Division administer first aid to soldiers wounded in the initial attacks at Utah Beach, France. June 6, 1944. *U.S. Army Photo*

be evacuated back to England immediately. Later, conditions permitting, the wounded could be held for seven, fifteen, even thirty days before being sent across the Channel.

At dawn, medics swarmed up onto the shellswept, bloody beaches of Normandy with the first three waves of Allied fighting men. They ran through the heavily mined beaches, vicious crossfire and sniper bullets to set up their little stations in the sand. Their losses were horrible, but they saved lives.

One of the lives saved was that of Edward Grigg, an eighteen-year-old machine-gunner in the 116th Infantry Regiment of the 29th Division. He remembers that day on Omaha Beach:

"An LST took us up to the beach and they just let those planks down and told us to get moving. Then all hell broke loose. Germans seemed to be everywhere and they started firing at us immediately. There wasn't a one of us who wasn't scared out of his mind.

"There was no place to run but forward. All that was behind us was water. You can talk about your heroes, but they, like all of us, worked on instinct. You didn't have time to think about it. I wouldn't have known my own dad if he'd been standing there next to me.

"Once you got a foothold at least you could start firing back. Mine was the first place I hit my foot on that land."

The unbelievable bloodshed lasted at least three or four hours before even the slightest progress was made.

"I can't explain how I stood it. You don't know what's going on at first and the longer you stay, the scareder you get. It was three days at least until I realized what I was doing."

Grigg will not forget the medics. "They were always right there with us." And one time, a medic by the name of Pete came to his aid after he'd given up all hope of living.

It happened just sixty-one days after the invasion. "Sixty-one days of watching your buddies drop like flies . . ." before Grigg too was cut down by the heavy fire of a tank gun outside the village of St.-Lô.

His right foot was blown off and his body riddled by eighteen shell fragments. A huge pleural-cavity wound was bleeding horribly. The pain was excrutiating because he was fully conscious. He hollered "Medic! Medic!" but he knew he was alone, buried in that mass of hedges and debris. Nobody could find him, he would bleed to death—but he kept calling out anyway.

Suddenly he heard a voice. "Take it easy, Eddie. Don't worry. I'll take care of you." It was Pete, the quiet little medic with whom he'd fought for the past sixty-one days.

Before Grigg knew it, Pete had cut off the shattered, dirty uniform and was applying tourniquets. Then he sprinkled sulpha on the wounds. After the bleeding had subsided, he gave young Grigg a shot of morphine, slung him over his shoulder and carried him to an abandoned farmhouse, where he laid him on a cot and covered him with blankets. "I gotta leave you now. Others need help, but I'll be back."

A few days later Pete himself was hauled into the hospital. He died just three beds away from the soldier whose life he had saved.*

Medics of the Army and Navy worked endless hours transporting casualties to England. Every possible means of carrying the wounded was used: DUKWs, LCVPs and LCTs. On D-day, fifty-four LSTs which had been converted for handling casualties shuttled back and forth with the agonized loads of men that the litter jeeps had brought. Landing boats, which had carried tanks, guns and men ashore, returned with wounded aboard. Up to 400 casualties were carried in one typical LST load.

Trips across the Channel were hell because of the bad

* From an interview with the author.

weather and the long span of fourteen hours it usually took. As time went on, casualties would be packed on deck and kept waiting for two or three days because of tides, bombings or storms. Corpsmen worked tirelessly trip after trip in all kinds of weather.

In order to avoid the enormous confusion of two-way traffic at the docks built at Portland (and to avoid displaying the morale-shattering wounded to new troops on their way over) the LSTs were met by smaller LCTs out in the harbor. The ships were "married," and corpsmen transferred the casualties. When the LCT was filled, it headed for the beach where litter bearers carried the wounded to ambulances. This amounted to three difficult and painful handlings of each man. But the wounded somehow accepted their fate and seldom complained. The sight of the white cliffs of Dover had a tremendous therapeutic effect.

As the Allied forces moved through France and into Germany, their medics went right along with them. Sergeant Short, en route to meet the invading forces, dropped out of formation whenever he saw a wounded man. Once he saw a man who'd been shot in the chest sitting on the side of the road. It was a ghastly wound, and Short was certain the soldier was done for. Nevertheless, he stopped and patched him up. Then he got word to the medical people of the 502d Regiment before marching on. (Short later saw the man in England. He was walking around, good as new.)

Airborne medic Charles Short took care of all kinds of people under all kinds of conditions. Things were really bad at the aid station they set up in an abandoned house near Bastogne. Casualties were heavy and facilities for treatment meager, but they did the best they could, using litters for treatment tables and other makeshift devices. It was the first time Short got sick from the goriness of it all.

Medics find an extra "window" as they peer from a house hit by German shellfire in Weisweiler, Germany. November 27, 1944. *U.S. Army Photo*

Medics often clowned around with each other when the going was so bad. It helped relieve a tension that, left unvented, could have exploded their minds. Short thought a lot of a little blond medic named Alquist because he was always pulling some dumb gag. There was the time Alquist came sloshing into the aid station all bundled up in parka and boots and announced, "The Germans are shouldering the eighty-eights [a huge artillery weapon]." Everybody chuckled, not knowing quite why, except that Alquist looked so green and young in all that heavy-weather equipment. And he was trying to talk big like the other soldiers. The "old man" didn't appreciate the humor, but he didn't say anything, either.

Young Alquist flapped his arms around for a while to get warm, had a couple of swigs of coffee, and then went out again.

A group of litter bearers take cover from sniper fire 700 yards from the Rapido River in Italy. January 22, 1944. *U.S. Army Photo*

That night, he heard a G.I. call for a medic from the snowy hillside, so he went after him. There was a shot. Next morning, Sergeant Short and the others from the aid station found Alquist. He was dead.

Allied forces suffered tragic losses at the Bulge. Always there was the scene of the medics setting up their aid stations in bombed-out buildings or abandoned houses. They scrubbed and cleaned them up as best they could and then waited for the wounded, who were not long in coming. Often they went after the casualties themselves. Short remembers one night they got a call that a wounded man needed help, so he got hold of a jeep and a medic named McCarthy and headed out. There was total darkness with no lights at all, so McCarthy went on foot ahead of the jeep and waved a white handkerchief to show Short where the road was. Suddenly they heard the word "Halt!"

The American sentry then gave the first part of the password and waited for the reply. But for some inexplicable reason, all McCarthy did at that moment was stumble around in the dark and mutter unintelligible sounds.

Short shouted in anger, "Dammit, McCarthy, give him the password!"

"I forgot it!"

The sentry suddenly realized they were medics. "Oh hell, let 'em go through."

The two finally got their wounded man back to the aid station at four in the morning.

Sergeant Charles Short survived the perilous preinvasion jump into France, although only thirty out of sixty of those airborne medics did. One man, Tom D'Andrea, broke his leg when he landed on the beach, but he continued ministering aid. He was awarded the Bronze Star. Van Volkenberg got the Distinguished Service Medal; Tech-5 Andrew Monger and Red Stewart both were awarded a Bronze Star. All have the gratitude of the countless men whom they tended. Short was commissioned

Sergeant DeWitt Blunt aids a wounded German near Coudray, France, August 7, 1944. *U.S. Army Photo*

in 1947, served in Korea and now holds the rank of major, Medical Service Corps.

When the going was really rough, there were the inevitable desertions among troops who just couldn't take it any more. These men, aware that the medics did not carry guns and therefore could not shoot them on sight, turned themselves in at the aid stations as prisoners.

There was often close contact between German and Allied medics, particularly toward the end of the war. Both sides took care of friend and foe alike. Each of them hung on to captured medics to care for their own wounded, and records indicate a great mutual respect between the two forces. The Germans who wore Red Cross armbands and bibs went to the same heroic ends as did the Allies so that their casualties might be saved.

Sergeant Hatten remembers one instance in which a German medic drove a one-horse haycart carrying two German patients and one American, right through the front lines to the American aid station. The man explained that the Germans had retreated beyond his station and he was now without supplies. His only interest was getting his patients to where they could have medical care.

As each town was captured and the Germans retreated, it was usually their medics who were the last to leave. At Weimar, a jeep driven by a G.I. was hailed by a young German woman wearing a medic uniform. She wanted to surrender herself and her patients because she could not take care of them any more. Neither would she desert them.

MEDAL OF HONOR[*]

From D-day, June 6, 1944, to V-E Day, May 7, 1945, the expeditionary forces under the command of General of the Army Dwight D. Eisenhower fought their way across France, through the Lowlands and into Germany. By the war's end, 129 Medal of Honor actions had taken place on the Continent. Among those honored was Private Harold A. Garman of the Fifth Medical Battalion.

On August 25, 1944, in the vicinity of Montereau, France, the enemy was sharply contesting any enlargement of the bridgehead which our forces had established on the northern bank of the Seine River. Casualties were being evacuated to the southern shore in assault boats paddled by litter bearers from a medical battalion. Private Garman, a litter bearer, was working on

[*] The following accounts are taken from Medal of Honor citations. Portions in quotation marks are verbatim.

the friendly shore carrying the wounded from the boats to waiting ambulances.

Suddenly, to his horror, he saw that a boatload of wounded which had reached midstream was under direct fire from a German machine gun. And the gun was only 100 yards away!

The men in the boat immediately rolled into the water and began to swim for shore. But there was one man who was so badly wounded he could not rise from his litter. Two other patients, who were unable to swim because of their wounds, clung to the sides of the boat.

Private Garman plunged into the Seine. Swimming directly into a hail of machine-gun bullets, he quickly reached the assault boat and then, while still under accurately aimed fire, towed the boat to safety on the southern shore.

"This soldier's moving heroism not only saved the lives of the three patients but so inspired his comrades that additional assault boats were immediately procured and the evacuation of the wounded resumed."

MEDAL OF HONOR (posthumous)

Private William D. McGee, a medical aidman with Company K, 304th Infantry, made a night crossing of the Moselle River on March 18, 1945, with troops bent on capturing the town of Mülheim, Germany. The enemy had retreated in the sector where the assault boats landed, but had left the shore heavily strewn with antipersonnel mines. Two men of the first wave, attempting to work their way forward, detonated mines that wounded them seriously, leaving them bleeding and in great pain beyond the reach of their comrades.

Entirely on his own initiative, Private McGee entered the mine field, brought out one of the injured to comparative safety, and had returned to rescue the second victim when he stepped on a mine and was severely wounded in the resulting explosion.

Although suffering intensely and bleeding profusely, he shouted orders that none of his comrades was to risk his life by entering the death-strewn field to render the first aid that might have saved his life.

MEDAL OF HONOR (posthumous)

Private First Class Frederick C. Murphy, an aidman with Company E, 259th Infantry, was wounded in the right shoulder soon after his comrades had jumped off in a dawn attack March 18, 1945, against the Siegfried Line at Saarlautern, Germany. He refused to withdraw for treatment and continued forward, administering first aid under heavy machine-gun, mortar and artillery fire. When the company ran into a thickly sown anti-personnel mine field and began to suffer more and more casualties, he continued to disregard his own wound and unhesitatingly braved the danger of exploding mines, moving about through heavy fire and helping the injured until he stepped on a mine that severed one of his feet. In spite of his grievous wounds, he struggled on with his work, refusing to be evacuated and crawling from man to man administering to them while in great pain and bleeding profusely. He was killed by the blast of another mine which he dragged himself across in an effort to reach still another casualty.

MEDAL OF HONOR (posthumous)

Technician Fifth Grade Alfred L. Wilson, while serving with the Medical Detachment, 328th Infantry, near Bezange la Petite, France, on November 8, 1944, volunteered to assist, as an aidman, a company other than his own. He administered to the wounded and returned to his own company when a shell burst, injuring a number of its men. While treating his comrades, he was seriously wounded but refused to be evacuated by litter bearers sent to relieve him. In spite of great pain and loss of blood, he continued to administer first aid until he was too weak to stand. Crawling from one patient to another, he continued his work until excessive loss of blood prevented him from moving. He then verbally directed unskilled enlisted men in first aid for the wounded. Still refusing assistance himself, he remained to instruct others in dressing the wounds of his comrades until he was unable to speak above a whisper and finally lapsed into unconsciousness. The effects of his injury later caused his death. By steadfastly remaining at the scene, Corporal Wilson was responsible for saving the lives of at least *ten* wounded men.

MEDAL OF HONOR

Corporal Thomas J. Kelly was an aidman with the First Platoon of Company C, 48th Armored Infantry Battalion, on April 5, 1945, during an attack on the town of Alemert, Germany. The platoon, committed in a flanking maneuver, had advanced down a small, open valley overlooked by wooded slopes hiding enemy machine guns and tanks, when the attack was stopped by murderous fire that inflicted heavy casualties in the American ranks. Ordered to withdraw, Corporal Kelly reached safety with the uninjured remnants of the unit but, on realizing the extent of casualties suffered by the platoon, voluntarily retraced his steps and began evacuating his comrades under direct machine-gun fire. He was forced to crawl, dragging the injured behind him for most of the 300 yards separating the exposed area from a place of comparative safety. Two other volunteers who attempted to negotiate the hazardous route with him were mortally wounded, but he kept on with his herculean task after dressing their wounds and carrying them to friendly hands. In all, he made ten separate trips through the brutal fire, each time bringing out a man from the death trap. Seven more casualties who were able to crawl by themselves he guided and encouraged in escaping from the hail of fire. After he had completed his heroic, self-imposed task and was near collapse from fatigue, he refused to leave his platoon until the attack had been resumed and the objective taken.

At the time of this action, Corporal Kelly was twenty-two years old.

7

World War II–in the Pacific

THE captain of the destroyer *Aaron Ward* studied the odd-looking conning tower through his binoculars. There were no identifying numbers or letters to indicate what country the submarine belonged to. But whatever the reason, cost or consequences, he knew he would have to destroy it because it was sailing in restricted waters outside the entrance to Pearl Harbor. His orders demanded this action.

The time was 6:45 A.M. and the date was December 7, 1941.

"Commence firing!"

The first shot was high. The second was a direct hit on the conning tower. Then the *Ward* swept past her target, almost running it down. She dropped four depth charges, and a towering geyser of gray-green water shot high into the air.

No one knew at that moment that the moving periscope, first sighted by the mine sweeper *Condor* and later by the *Antares*, both of whom reported their observations to the *Ward*, belonged to a country about to wage a sneak attack on Pearl Harbor. The mystery of the strange submarine was not solved just then, but was most assuredly dissolved.

At Kahuku Point on the northern tip of Oahu, two Army privates operating the radar in a mobile unit picked up a blip 130 miles away. It was the biggest they had ever seen, and they immediately reported to the duty officer. "Don't worry about it. It's probably some B-17's coming in from the States." Nevertheless, the two privates continued to track the blips until the signals were twenty-two miles away, when they were lost in the "dead zone" of surrounding hills.

Elsewhere that morning, a messenger boy pedaled his bicycle in the direction of the naval station. He carried a telegram from General George C. Marshall, Chief of Staff in Washington, D.C., to the commanding officer of Pearl Harbor. The telegram warned the naval station to be on the alert for a Japanese attack.

The U.S. Pacific Fleet rested quietly in the harbor. In all, there were seventy warships, including eight of their nine battleships. Besides the battleships, there were two heavy cruisers, six light cruisers, twenty-nine destroyers, five submarines, a gunboat, nine mine layers and ten mine sweepers. There were twenty-four auxiliary ships: tenders, oilers, tugs, ammunition and supply ships. Also on the island were 200 Army planes, lined up on the field, wingtip to wingtip, fifty Marine Corps planes and 150 Navy planes.

Aboard the U.S.S. *Nevada*, the ship's band on the fantail had just played "The Star-Spangled Banner" as the Sunday flag was hoisted. Ensign Joseph Taussig took over the eight-to-twelve watch, called the log room and told them to light off another boiler since the steaming boiler had been on for four days. Sailors in whites lined up for liberty: the softball team wanted a boat to take them to Aiea Recreation Field, his messmates wanted a boat to take them to Ford Island and the garbage lighter was standing in to take their garbage. In their wake came a motor launch from the *Arizona* with garbage to dump. Everything seemed to be happening at once.

Taussig peered into the distance at the *Helena* across the bay.

Smoke was pouring from her, and at first he thought the ship was blowing tubes while the wind was too strong. Then he decided it was on fire!

He called for the boatswain's mate, but as he did so, he saw a torpedo plane flying toward the battleships; it was carrying a "fish." Flabbergasted, he watched it drop and hit a ship. Was it a mistake? Who? And what to do?

Adolpho Solar, the boatswain's mate, said, "Mr. Taussig, they're bombing Ford Island!"

General Quarters! Bugler! Boatswain's mate! He ran for the alarm switch and at the same time Solar boomed out the word. "Man your general quarters stations on the double! This is no drill! We are being attacked by aircraft! Foreign aircraft!"

Pharmacist's Mate Second Class Ned Curtis was on duty in

December 7, 1941. The *Arizona* was in flames. The *Nevada* managed to get under way following the sneak attack by the Japanese. She was later beached. Corpsmen saved many lives that day. *U.S. Navy Photo*

the sick bay when he heard the call. Since this was his battle station, he quickly secured the ports. The other ten corpsmen aboard, some of whom had been sleeping in the sick bay, ran to their preassigned battle dressing stations. There were three doctors on the *Nevada*: Commander Ed Goodbody, Lieutenant Jerome Zobel and Lieutenant Robert Freyling. Lieutenant Commander Curtiss Schantz was the dental officer.

At 0802 the *Nevada's* machine guns opened fire on the torpedo planes approaching on the port beam, but to little avail. At 0803 a torpedo struck the bow, portside, and three minutes later several bombs fell close aboard. Three minutes after that, the *Arizona* alongside was afire.

Meanwhile, Ensign Taussig had scrambled up the ladder to the boat deck, pulled himself into the doorway of his gun director and put on his earphones. No orders came through. Then the guns started shooting. He yelled out the doorway for numbers three and five to take director control and one and seven to take local. It was his own private system and had never been used, but for the situation he thought it highly ingenious. Watching through his checksight after he'd picked up a plane, he made a setup, but the plane disappeared in the smoke shortly afterward. Taussig felt smug about that. He looked out the door for new planes to conquer and noticed that his director, the starboard mount, was swung over to the port side so that his guns were firing over the ship structure! He silently blessed the individual who'd had sense enough to pull the firing cutouts, which as a peacetime safety precaution prevented them from firing over a sixty-five-degree gun elevation.

Suddenly Taussig felt a sharp blow on his leg and the bottom of his foot. It were as though someone had hit him with a sledgehammer. He was later to guess that it was a chunk of the *Arizona*, which had just been blown up. At any rate, his thigh was fractured and his knee was about eight inches from his hip because of muscle contraction. There was no feeling at all in his leg. Before he knew it, he had fallen out of the director, twisting so as to break the fall with his chest.

The men picked him up, carried him away from the gun blasts into the fire-control shack and laid him on the deck.

Ships all around them were being sunk. The *Arizona* was a blazing inferno. The *Nevada* fought back with everything she had, but Taussig was helpless. His trousers were split from his hip to his knee, so he ripped them away and tried to put a tourniquet around his badly bleeding leg, but the wound was too high. So he grasped the front of his leg with his left hand and held the lips of the wound together as blood oozed through his fingers.

Below, in sick bay, PhM2c Ned Curtis heard the call from sky control up on the superstructure. "The O.D. has been injured! He needs help!"

A whole series of thoughts jumped into Curtis' mind. Such a call was contrary to doctrine; the crew up there was supposed to give the man aid and then evacuate him to the dressing station. But book rules wouldn't work here. He grabbed his first-aid pouch and ran.

Strangely enough, Curtis felt no fear at the time he raced across the deck in the midst of machine-gun fire and flying shrapnel to climb the main mast to the fire-control director. His only thought was to get up there, as quickly as possible. Two decks above the quarterdeck, he found Taussig. The man was bleeding badly, so Curtis tied a tourniquet on the leg and applied a large battle dressing to the wound.

At 0830, a bomb hit the bridge and penetrated to the forecastle deck, causing a tremendous shock to the entire ship. Fires ignited on the bridge and below deck. And still the crew of the *Nevada* fought bravely on. Taussig, realizing the precarious position of the handful of men who stayed with him, ordered everyone out, including Curtis, but no one would leave.

By 0840, the *Nevada* was under way, at various speeds and on various courses conforming to the channel. Curtis, realizing they would be passing the burning *Arizona,* dipped cotton into water for the men to hold over their noses as a kind of filter against the stinging smoke. The *Nevada,* with her guns still blazing, was going to try to get out of that trap, come hell or high water. But the Japanese spotted her and at 0850 concentrated their fire.

Hits on the forecastle exploded below decks; one or two were near the crews' galley. Now there was fire foreward and amidship.

Corpsmen worked frantically at the battle dressing stations as the wounded and injured poured in. The central battle dressing station was secured when smoke filled the compartment and made it unusable. At least six men were overcome, evacuated and revived. One chief petty officer suffered a heart attack as he was sitting at a table wearing his gas mask.

In the after-battle dressing station, there were twenty-four cases of burns, fractures, and gunshot wounds, while in the sick bay, thirty cases were treated: an amputated leg, two compound fractures, an amputated hand, three chest and shoulder wounds, fifteen shrapnel wounds, along with neck, back and other lacerations. Corpsmen and seamen administered artificial respiration to those who had been overcome by smoke. The dental and medical storerooms were now under water . . .

Curtis does not know whose decision it was to get Taussig out of that hut on the superstructure. Smoke and fire were coming up all around. In another moment it would be unbearable. But how to move a severely injured officer down ladders that were hellishly hot from fire and smoke?

There was a Stokes litter attached to a nearby smokestack. The men put Taussig into it and Curtis wrapped him in blankets. Then after tying a rope to it, the young pharmacist's mate descended the ladders so that he could guide it as it came down. It was a painful, searing experience, but the injured man was finally taken to an area of comparative safety.

The ship's log states in cryptic terms: "0907 bomb hit forecastle killing Chief Boatswain E. J. Hill (blown overboard) and an unknown number of men. Tugs fought fires in wardroom country and forward. Casualties were transferred to the hospital ship *Solace* and the Naval hospital at Pearl Harbor. At 1015, there was no progress in overcoming the fires forward. Stern began swinging to the middle of the channel."

As history now shows, the *Nevada* was deliberately beached in order to prevent its blocking the channel to Pearl Harbor.

There were many awards for the men of that gallant ship. Pharmacist's Mate Ned Curtis received the Navy Cross for his care of the wounded throughout the ship and for his heroic performance in saving the life of Ensign Taussig. Curtis was later hospitalized with first-, second- and third-degree burns on his legs and arms, suffered while guiding the ensign's stretcher down those fireswept ladders. He remained in the Navy and after twenty-four years' service became the first Medical Service Corps student at the Naval War College at Newport, Rhode Island. He now holds the rank of Captain, MSC, USN.*

For the battleship *Nevada*, Admiral C. W. Nimitz said as he presented the awards, "If a ship has a personality and a soul, and I am convinced that she has, what a proud moment this must be for this gallant ship." The *Nevada*, though she lost 180 men from a battery of 220, was the only ship to get under way with her guns still blazing.

The casualty count at Pearl Harbor was 4,575 Americans dead, injured or missing in the attack. Eighteen American warships, including seven of the eight battleships, were sunk or badly damaged. The cruisers *Raleigh, Helena* and *Honolulu*

---

* From an interview with the author.

were crippled; three destroyers were wrecked. Out of 400 planes, 188 were destroyed and 159 damaged.

On the following day, President Franklin D. Roosevelt asked the Congress of the United States to declare war on the empire of Japan.

The United States paid dearly for the mistakes made at Pearl Harbor. For a while it seemed the Japanese would capture the entire Pacific, with little or no resistance.

Guam, the Philippines, Hong Kong, Singapore, Wake and Midway fell almost immediately. By May 1942 the Japanese had captured the Netherlands East Indies, Sumatra, Borneo, Java, Celebes, Amboina, Bali and Timor. They had seized Salamaua on the coast of northeast New Guinea and were now working their way island by island through the Solomons toward Tulagi and Guadalcanal.

But the Japanese had made a serious mistake during their sneak attack on Pearl Harbor. They had not harmed the "tank farm" underground fuel supply, or seriously damaged the submarine base and shipyard. They soon made another bad mistake: splitting their powerful force of six aircraft carriers in two in order to support their drives toward Port Moresby on New Guinea and Tulagi—and Midway.

The Allies dared not lose Port Moresby because that would have rendered Australia practically unusable. On May 7, when the Japanese moved in to take the port, the United States Navy challenged them in a furious air and sea battle which lasted for thirty hours. The price paid for Port Moresby was appallingly high; the *Lexington* was sunk, the *Yorktown* damaged and two smaller warships sunk. There were 543 casualties at the now-famed Battle of the Coral Sea, but the enemy, for the first time, had been halted. The Battle of Midway, which followed in June, was an unqualified victory for the United States Navy.

The repaired *Yorktown* was ready to go again. She, along with the *Enterprise*, the *Hornet*, seven heavy cruisers and fourteen destroyers, shattered Tojo's mad dream of unchecked conquest in the Pacific.

It was eight months after the bombing of Pearl Harbor that the First Marine Division went ashore at Lunga Point in Guadalcanal and at little Tulagi Island. Ten thousand green leathernecks (half soldier, half sailor and all scrapper) sharpened their knives and bayonets, checked their .50-and .30-caliber machine guns, mortars, packstraps, ammunition belts, barbed wire, jeeps and rations and stormed the shore of the twenty-five-mile wide, ninety-mile long island. Their accompanying corpsmen checked their aid kits, field packs and other gear. They made sure their Red Cross arm bands were clearly visible. Then they went right along with the assault force. Six thousand other Marines headed for Tulagi, making four separate landings including two on Florida Island. The Allied offensive in the Pacific had begun.

No one knew much about the kinds of enemies they would fight in the South Pacific. Americans had a few vague ideas about swaying palms, white sand and sarong-clad dancing girls. The *National Geographic* had pictured interesting natives with odd, fuzzy hair styles. The Malarial Commission of the Rockefeller Foundation had made a report covering the period 1930–40 which the Medical Department had carefully studied. But this was about the only information available on the regions where hundreds of thousands of men would fight in the years to come.

Another mystery was that of the Japanese soldier himself. What kind of a fighter was he? How did he think or feel? His eyes were slanted and his skin was dark. He had a reputation for atrocities in China, the Philippines and other places where he had been the victor. His country bombed Pearl Harbor. This was generally the hazy picture that the teenage Marines and

Foxhole surgery and plasma administered by enlisted Navy corpsmen saved countless lives in the South Pacific. *U.S. Navy Photo*

freshly schooled corpsmen carried with them into Guadalcanal.

The answers to these mysteries did not come immediately. Because of the surprise element, the landing on Tulagi was comparatively smooth. There were fewer enemy troops on Guadalcanal than had been expected, and although there was token resistance, the situation seemed to be well in hand. But when Japanese headquarters learned what had happened, they sent a powerful naval task force of five heavy cruisers, two light cruisers and a destroyer to go after the United States Navy ships that had supported the landings. Still bottled up in "the slot," the narrow waters between Guadalcanal and Florida Island where they were unable to maneuver, they were easy targets for the enemy attack at 1:30 in the morning. The Allies lost four cruisers, the *Vincennes, Quincy, Astoria* and the Australian

Canberra. Part of the bow was blown off the *Chicago*, and the destroyer *Talbot* was hit. There was nothing to do but withdraw, taking the transports with them.

For the Marines ashore, this meant the loss of unloaded supplies and troops who were waiting to be ferried ashore. The First Marines were virtually isolated with about four days' supply of ammunition, a limited food supply and a shortage of medical supplies, should the fighting really get heavy. There were also spare parts for jeeps, guns and other equipment inauspiciously moved out to sea. In time, over-age converted transports and daring pilots flying unarmed planes did run the dangerous "slot" even as the Japanese kept the island under continual bombardment.

In ten days, a 1,000-man Japanese force landed twenty miles east of Henderson Field. Another 4,000 were on their way. Three weeks later, another Japanese force landed eleven miles from Henderson Field with 1,000 more troops.

Night after night, week after week, the Japanese pounded away at the exhausted, beleaguered leathernecks. There was no respite, particularly at night. And as the struggle continued, the American Marine and corpsman got to know their enemies—intimately.

The young corpsman from Oshkosh, Tampa or Altoona could not at first understand how anyone could kill another person who was wounded and helpless. He could not fathom a soldier's ignoring a comrade's cry for help. He himself, admittedly an idealist, believed that as a noncombatant he need only concentrate his efforts on saving lives and alleviating pain of men on both sides who were in need of care. This is what the books said. This is the way things had gone at the Geneva Convention.

The Navy hospital corpsmen at Guadalcanal were among the first to learn that here was a new breed of enemy. The fanatical Nipponese cared nothing for human life, not even their own. For instance, these people made no rescue attempts for downed airmen as we did. Their fliers simply died of injuries or were drowned. Soldiers preferred suicide by jumping over cliffs to being captured. A wounded Japanese, if he could not be moved during a retreat, was cared for in the manner of ancient wars: his carotid artery was cut and his body covered with an inflammable fluid, then set afire.

The young, untried corpsman learned something else, too. His bright Red Cross emblem made a perfect target, so he got rid of that almost as he raced up the beach the first day. He got himself a gun because he learned that the Japanese would shoot him unless he shot first. He became skilled with a knife, but not in the way he would have preferred. And he got used to the deliberate attacks on his aid stations, ambulances and even his helpless litter patients. He saw wounded Japanese knife American doctors who were trying to care for them. They attacked him, too, as he desperately tied the lifesaving tourniquets on their bleeding limbs. And he did his best to outsmart the enemy out there in the dark who would whimper in an all-American accent, "Corpsman! Corpsman! Come and get me. I need help!" Sometimes he ran into that hail of fire; other times he was able to take a nose count of his men and know this was a ruse.

The Japanese were excellent jungle fighters. They tolerated the climate, the bugs, the infections. They were familiar with and even immune to dozens of strange diseases that stalked the men from Maine, California, Kansas and Minnesota. Disease was aligned on the side of the Japanese at Guadalcanal.

Men living like rats in the dirt could not wash their clothes for days following the invasion. With the high humidity, perspiration and suffocating heat, their clothes never got dry. They scratched and tore at their aggravated skin until they had ugly open sores. Corpsmen, when they weren't on patrol or tending desperate wounds or giving shots of morphine or administering plasma, painted the men's "jungle rot" with gentian violet.

Guadalcanal. Corpsmen carry a wounded man back from the front line. *U.S. Marine Corps Photo*

Native children receive medical attention from Navy doctors and corpsmen. Solomon Islands, August 7, 1943. *U.S. Navy Photo*

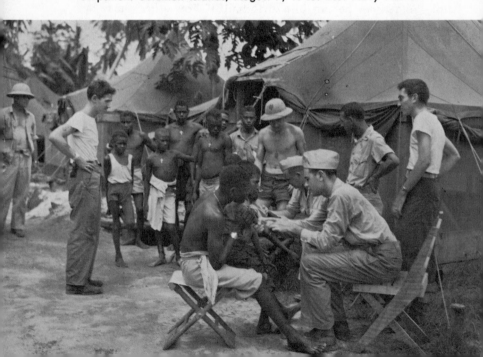

The six-foot-high *kunai* grass that grows in the South Pacific resembles a Midwest field of waving wheat—from a distance or from the air. It is beautiful to look at, but not to live with. *Kunai* makes an excellent breeding area for lice, and these lice, which are not a European variety and were therefore unknown, spread a vicious disease known as scrub typhus. Little could be done to help the victim as paralysis set in the legs and worked up toward the lungs. In seven days, a patient could not move, and if he had not recovered by the twelfth day, he was gone.

Heat exhaustion was common. So were foot infections. Hookworm was almost as common as the common cold. Epidemic gastroenteritis, catarrhal fever and dengue moved in. It was almost as if the clock had been turned back to the days when battles were lost not by bullets but by disease. The worst disease of all on Guadalcanal was malaria. The number of infected men may never be determined, but it is safe to assume that almost every man who served on that island during the period from August 7, 1942, to February 9, 1943, fell victim to the disease. Almost 9,000 of those troops were hospitalized with disease at one time or another, although out of necessity front-line troops weren't even allowed a reduction to light duty unless their fever was higher than 103 degrees.

One reason for the high incidence of malaria was the unfortunate choice of bivouac area in the low, wet, mosquito-infested jungle. The disease was also brought into the area by infected native workers. Doctors and corpsmen did what they could to halt the spread, but it was difficult to convince a young Marine who was fighting night and day for his very life that a malaria-preventive atabrine tablet was as important to his survival as his weapon. It became the corpsman's task to stand at the chow line, hand out a pill to each man and check to see that he swallowed it before he got anything to eat. This was known as "pill call." Whenever possible, pill call was extended to the local villagers.

The corpsman's role in the South Pacific was different from that of the Army medic in Europe because he seldom had a nearby safe place to send his casualties. In later campaigns hospital ships, anchored in the harbor, could receive the wounded and give them care, but there was no such luxury at Guadalcanal. Because field hospitals were targets for almost daily aerial bombing or artillery fire or both, it became necessary to evacuate patients by sea or by air a distance of some hundreds of miles before operations and other definitive measures could be carried out.

Aid stations in these islands were often no more than a group of protective trees, or slit trenches from which corpsmen could crawl to get the wounded and drag them back by a rope tied around them. Once in the trench, casualties could be given plasma and first aid. But the trenches were in constant danger of being overrun or surrounded by Japanese in *banzai* charges. In an absolutely quiet night, they'd creep up and drop grenades into foxholes or "aid stations."

The usual method of evacuating patients was to carry them by hand on stretchers to the rear, where they would be placed in the first available transportation, such as jeeps or ammunition trucks. From there, they would be carried to ambulances or directly to the field hospital. Litter squads consisted of four men because of the often necessary long carries through the jungle. Once the patient had been brought to the "beach," there were further problems of transportation. Lack of communication between ship and shore caused many inequities in apportioning the casualties. Some ships failed to fly the Mike flag that would indicate they could take wounded abroad. Transport planes that could accommodate eighteen stretcher patients or thirty-six ambulatory ones began making their daring flights through the flak-filled air to evacuate battle victims. Aboard the planes were specially trained nurses and corpsmen. September 18, they had flown 147 patients out of Guadalcanal.

The men who serve in the United States Marine Corps are extremely proud. In battle, they are fierce and unforgiving toward those whose courage does not match their own. Lieutenant General Lewis C. Walt, now Commanding General of the Third Marine Amphibious Forces and the Navy Component Command of the Military Assistance Command of Vietnam, was a major at the time he landed at Tulagi. He knew his corpsmen well at that time and later all through the other bloody campaigns in the Pacific. Other corpsmen were with him in Korea. And now he observes them in Vietnam. "I can't say enough to praise them.... They out-Marine a Marine by volunteering for all kinds of jobs, including more than their share of patrols. The spirit they have is absolutely amazing. They are proud and dedicated and the Marines think the world of them. Why, a Marine platoon would no more go into battle without corpsmen than without weapons. The fact that they know corpsmen are there to take care of them is a tremendous morale factor."

General Walt was commander of the Second Battalion, Fifth Marines during the third big battle at Guadalcanal on November 5, 1942. A river formed the dividing line between the Japanese and American forces. On the coastal area next to the ocean were palms, dense jungle and steep terrain, but the enemy went into it, hoping to capture the Marines from the rear. The battle became famous as "Edson's Ridge."

General Walt was with Shorty, the corpsman in the beach area. Suddenly, about 125 feet in front of them, a hidden machine gun opened up and Shorty's tentmate was shot. He began calling for a corpsman, and Shorty, recognizing the voice, asked permission to go after him.

"I can't let you go," Walt told him. "The machine gun is hidden. It would be suicide."

The cries went on for about fifteen minutes. Finally Shorty

said, "Major, I can't take it any longer. I know I'll get killed but I gotta go to him."

Walt grabbed for Shorty and got hold of his dungarees, but the young corpsman tore out of his grasp. He ran to his friend and, as he knelt to tend him, was killed by the rain of five bullets.*

General Walt recommended many corpsmen for decorations and awards. One of them was Pharmacist's Mate Third Class Albern M. Potter, who accompanied the assault group at Tulagi. He received the Navy Cross "for extraordinary heroism in action against the enemy, during the hostile attacks on the night of September 13, 1942, at Guadalcanal when, as company corpsman attached to a front line company, he constantly exposed himself to enemy fire, at times from all directions, to care for and evacuate the wounded. As a result of this devotion to duty, outstanding bravery and utter disregard for his own personal safety, many lives were undoubtedly saved."

Potter was later stricken with malaria and hookworm. Following hospitalization in Australia, he returned to his battalion and served in other South Pacific campaigns. After the war, he remained in the Navy and now holds the rank of chief warrant officer.

By December 1942, the First Marine Division, worn out after four months of almost nonstop fighting, got relief. Division casualties amounted to 605 officers and men killed in action, 76 dead of wounds or missing, and 1,278 wounded. Disease or injuries, or both, had hospitalized 9,000. Cruel lessons were learned that would profit hundreds of thousands of men in the campaigns yet to come.

During World War II, Navy corpsmen served on land in hospitals and dispensaries, with the Fleet Marine Force, aboard

* From an interview with the author.

warships, in airplanes evacuating the wounded, and in submarines.

The principal target of Allied submarines operating in the Pacific was not Japanese warships but merchant vessels carrying raw materials—iron, tin, rubber and food from conquered Thailand, Sumatra and Malaya to the Japanese homeland. They also stalked troop ships and tankers sailing for ports in their far-flung Pacific empire. The United States Navy fleet submarine was a comparatively small, cigar-shaped boat, the top of which was a flat deck. Rising from the center of the deck was the conning tower, which contained the steering wheel, instruments and the navigating officer's equipment. On top of the conning tower was the captain's bridge.

The fleet submarine of this period had two hulls. The outside pressure hull was designed to resist water pressure. Between the two hulls were tanks for ballast, or water used for making the submarine heavy so that it would submerge. What was left inside for a seventy-five-man crew to subsist, fight and work in was a carefully planned, efficiently crammed, highly organized, elongated compartment. With space at a premium, torpedomen usually slept right next to their weapons.

The medical department aboard these boats consisted of one chief pharmacist's mate. His responsibilities were often heavy ones, particularly in combat. He took care of his shipmates who were injured during the lightning-like maneuvers necessary to clear the bridge in the relatively few seconds that elapsed between the time the diving signal was given and the submarine submerged. Crushed fingers, broken ribs, dislocations, bruised shoulders and lacerations of various degrees resulted from the sudden exodus of men from the bridge through a twenty-four-inch hatch, and down the slippery and precipitous ladder into the conning tower.

The submarine corpsman had very little space in which to work and to store his medical supplies. Yet he did an outstanding job in a variety of ways. For instance, during World War II, submarines rescued 549 survivors in air-sea operations. At least half of these people required medical aid from the pharmacist's mate.

The crew of the submarine often worked under immense stress. Hunting the prey under forced inactivity in an environment of heat and high humidity, during times when all air-conditioning and ventilation systems had to be turned off, wore at men's nerves. A submarine log explains a typical operation: "A terrific explosion jarred the boat. All hands not holding on to something were knocked from their feet. At three hundred thirty feet, fire broke out in the maneuvering room . . . all power was lost. Thick toxic smoke filled the maneuvering room and after-torpedo rooms. All hands aft were sick. We went up and down three times and had started down the fourth time before power was regained. In the maneuvering room the situation was bad. All hands were violently ill. For the first two hours we were in a mighty tough spot. Extreme discomfort was suffered from the accumulation of heat and humidity. All hands stripped down to shorts and the men took off their shoes and socks. The predicament of the boat was fully recognized by the older and more experienced men. As the youngsters folded up, the others took over. The most startling effect was the apathy engendered by the combination of heat, pressure, physical effort and mental stress. Some without permission, others after requesting relief, would seek the closest clear spot on deck, lie down and fall asleep. Often following a depth charge attack, men would have nausea, vomiting and abdominal cramps."

Probably no other single disease caused more anxiety to submarine personnel than appendicitis. Because medical officers were not carried on submarines, it became important to formulate and promulgate a policy governing the treatment of appendicitis. All pharmacist's mates in the submarine service and those in the "School for Pharmacist's Mates Entering the Submarine Service" were impressed with the fact that in untrained hands, the diagnosis of appendicitis is difficult and that gastrointestinal disturbances and constipation, which are common in submarine personnel, add to the difficulty in diagnosis. The orders, "Never resort to surgery" and "Never give a cathartic to a patient suspected of having appendicitis" were put into effect toward the end of the first year of the war, and a conservative method of treatment was outlined.

Regardless of the order not to perform appendectomies on board submarines, the operation was found necessary on several occasions. An appendectomy was done by a pharmacist's mate aboard the U.S.S. *Sea Dragon* on September 11, 1942. Prior to the operation, which lasted three hours, the patient had been ill for fourteen days. The incident is believed to be the first of its kind in submarine history. While this case had a happy ending, the Navy hastens to point out that this particular pharmacist's mate had considerable experience in assisting in surgical operations. "It is hoped that his success will not encourage others to take such risks. . . ."

In another instance on board the U.S.S. *Grayback* in December 1942, the patient had been ill for about forty-eight hours before he was operated on. At the operation, which lasted about one and a half hours, the appendix was found to be ruptured. Sulfanilamide powder was instilled, drainage was instituted by the insertion of an elastic rubber band and the abdomen was closed. Ether, administered by a submarine escape-lung mouthpiece, was used as an anesthetic. Spoons were flattened for use as retractors and long-nose pliers from the engine room were also among the makeshift instruments. For the "operating room nurse," the pharmacist's mate called on the services of a motor machinist's mate, first class.

In the third instance, an operation for appendicitis was performed aboard the U.S.S. *Silversides* on December 22, 1942. The patient had been ill for about twelve hours prior to the operation, which was performed on the wardroom table with the submarine submerged at 100 feet. The effectiveness of the spinal anesthetic soon wore off, so "ether was administered, following the directions on the can." This anesthetized the operating "staff" as well as the patient. One hour after completion (the operation lasted four hours), the *Silversides* tangled with a destroyer. The patient was convalescing the following morning to the tune of torpedo firing, two depth-charge attacks, two "crash dives" and an aerial bombing that knocked him out of his bunk. Naval records indicate that "the conduct of the patient was exemplary. . . ."

Pharmacists mates made diagnoses of appendicitis on 116 war patrols in 127 instances during the entire war. Throughout the war in the submarine force, not one death from appendicitis was reported. Commanding officers were so impressed with the performance of their pharmacist's mates in handling these emergencies that in twenty-two instances they were specially commended.

Meanwhile, corpsmen were in action aboard surface vessels. The U.S.S. *Pecos*, a refueling ship, was ordered to intercept two destroyers that picked up 450 survivors from the *Langley*, which had been hit by Kamikaze attacks. The weather was bad and the seas rough; the time was four o'clock in the morning. But the survivors, all of whom were suffering from shock and exposure, were finally transferred from the rocking, rolling destroyers to the *Pecos*. One medical officer and five corpsmen worked frantically, treating shock, applying splints and bandaging wounds. But the story wasn't yet over for the survivors—or the medical personnel.

Six hours later, enemy bombers appeared overhead. A great hole was torn into the side of the *Pecos,* and the ship began to sink. The injured men in the forward part of the ship could not reach the dressing station where the doctor and four of his corpsmen were at work, so the pharmacist's mate carried on alone. Newly burned and injured patients were brought to the already crowded sick bay.

The doctor describes their predicament: "When I heard the machine and antiaircraft guns rattle, I knew that we had about thirty seconds before we would sustain another hit or

The U.S.S. *Santa Fe* lay alongside the U.S.S. *Franklin,* rendering assistance after the carrier had been hit and set afire by a Japanese dive bomber. The wounded were transported by stretcher but a large number of men came aboard across the bow loading to the top of number 2 five-inch mount. This mount was damaged badly against the side of the carrier. Many men went across over the radio antennas and by swinging on lines rigged on the underside of the flight deck. Hose shown here was severed twice by the U.S.S. *Santa Fe* crashing into it. Corpsmen received and cared for the wounded and injured. March 19, 1945. *U.S. Navy Photo*

near miss. We would treat a patient for a few moments and then drop down alongside him, the pharmacist's mate on one side and I on the other and wait for the ship to jump. As soon as the ship stopped shuddering we would again attend the injured until the next bomb burst. Often the interval was less than a couple of minutes.

"After four hours we were ordered to abandon ship. The injured officers and men were carried from the sick bay up the slanting deck to the side of the ship. Kapok-filled mattresses were lashed to those most severely injured and then lowered over the side. A well man accompanied each injured man into the water. Men tore down doors and broke out wooden panels to obtain floatable supports. Others made use of bamboo poles which the commanding officer had taken aboard before leaving Tjilatjap; one ten-foot pole gave support to four men."*

There was no other vessel in the vicinity when the *Pecos* went down at two o'clock that afternoon. Survivors set off flares, hoping for rescue, and finally one of the destroyers which had transferred the *Langley* survivors to the *Pecos* just ten hours earlier arrived at the scene. Again, there was the painful and harrowing movement of wounded and injured men from ship to ship. By the time the medical officer and corpsmen from the *Pecos* got aboard the destroyer, the chief pharmacist's mate had laid out all their medical equipment on the table in the officer's wardroom. It was one o'clock in the morning before all men had been taken aboard and cared for.

July, 1943. New Georgia. Navy corpsmen serving with the First Marine Raider Regiment learned that some of their worst problems involved *getting* to the scene of action. The medical section consisting of three medical officers and thirty-two corpsmen landed with the Marines about 500 yards up the Punda-

* From official Navy records.

kona River, where they bivouacked in the driving rain until daylight. At six in the morning, after discarding bedrolls and gas masks, the northern landing group began their march to Dragons Peninsula. The movement from the Pundakona River to the Giza-giza River was made over three parallel trails previously cut by natives with the First Raider battalion in the lead. Marines with their corpsmen marched over huge fallen logs, branches of trees, roots and vines. They crossed swamps and mud, and climbed up and down steep coral hills. It took the men ten long hours to make those eight miles through the jungle.

At last they reached the Giza-giza River, but by this time the men were so exhausted and thoroughly soaked by heavy rain they simply dropped to the ground and slept in their ponchos. By nightfall of the following day, they had crossed another river and camped in a swamp with no protection from the elements. At 0800, July 7, 1943, led by native guides, the battalion moved out through mangrove swamps, over fallen trees, banyan roots and coral outcroppings. The troops became so exhausted that they threw away all unnecessary gear and a portion of their food consisting of K and D rations.

Corpsmen on this route could carry no plasma. Their only medical supplies were those carried in their pouches and in the individual first-aid kits issued each Marine.

At 0700, July 10, the battalion closed in on Enogai. Now, at last they were in heavy action. At the time of battle, the men had had no food and only one canteen of water for thirty hours.

Corpsmen did what they could, but the situation was bad.

There were no hospital facilities where they could send their wounded until four weeks after the campaign began. There was no air evacuation until August. The nearest hospital was Guadalcanal, which was 200 miles away, and twenty hours by boat. Transportation through the jungle was a horrible ordeal for

Malaria was a serious medical problem in the South Pacific campaigns. Corpsmen sprayed swamps near camp so that the coating of oil would kill the mosquito larvae. *U.S. Navy Photo*

Wounded at Tarawa. Marines wounded in the landing on Tarawa are towed out to a larger craft on a rubber boat by their buddies. The larger vessels took them to base hospitals for expert medical care. November, 1943, Second Marine Division. *U.S. Marine Corps Photo*

both patients and litter bearers. Six men were required to carry one litter, and they had to stop to rest every 300 or 400 yards. Patients often died en route.

Flies, mosquitoes and infections harassed the combat troops and corpsmen alike. In New Georgia, combat fatigue was prevalent. During a three-month period, beginning June 30, there were some 2,500 men carrying a diagnosis of anxiety reaction.

At long last, Americans were able to move their casualties out of that hellhole to where they could receive further medical treatment. During a four-month period, 8,225 patients were evacuated by air and 7,300 by sea.

Navy corpsmen suffered heavy casualties in New Georgia. One lost was Pharmacist's Mate Thaddeus Parker, who was killed instantly as he rushed between lines to administer first aid to a badly wounded Marine during the action at Bairoko. This brave act, a source of inspiration to his fellow corpsmen and to the men of his company, served, however, to point out the importance of training troops to crawl back from the lines when wounded. On many occasions, men only slightly wounded called for help, and when their buddies or corpsmen went to their aid, they too were shot and injured or killed. Troops and corpsmen were cautioned not to go out in front of the line to get the wounded unless the lines were stationary, or unless a withdrawal was being made or contemplated. If troops were advancing, the wounded would be behind the lines in a relatively short time.

This policy, although a sensible and sane one, was not carried out at that time. It probably never will be.

The attack on Tarawa began November 20, 1943. It was a violent and bloody battle between American leathernecks and 4,000 first-rate Japanese soldiers, most of whom were concentrated on Betio Island at Tarawa's southwestern tip. The sliver of land bristled with coastal defense guns, machine guns, anti-landing obstacles and barbed wire. Added to these defenses were the surrounding reefs, on which landing craft grounded far out from the beach. Marines were forced to wade in as far as 500 yards in some places. Those who made it to shore found little safe cover. Some companies lost up to three-fourths of their men.

Experience had taught the medical forces that the only effective and efficient manner of handling the wounded in these Pacific campaigns was to get them out of there to a safe area in the rear. Careful plans were made, methods drawn up, but because of the huge numbers of casualties, there was at first no organized system of evacuation. The men were simply taken out to the AP ships in the harbor by any and all possible means: amphibious tractors or available boats. Meanwhile, corpsmen, using only what medical supplies they carried in their kits or boat bags, dug into the sand alongside their patients and administered aid as the battle raged on.

By D-day at noon, 300 troops had secured a small area on Red Beach Two adjacent to the pier. A small number of troops were landed on this beach in the afternoon and evening of the same day. By D-day plus one, about 100 yards of the beach had been secured—but only to a depth of twenty-five to seventy-five feet.

By morning of D-day plus one, the main points of evacuation had been established and were functioning. Additional medical supplies and troops were landed to augment the small force ashore.

In the four days of the attack on Tarawa, 2,500 casualties were evacuated by ship and by Navy flying boats. And, again utilizing experience gained from previous campaigns, massive quantities of plasma (4,000 units) were used to prevent shock and save the lives of Marines who otherwise might have died. This averages out to two units of plasma per casualty during this period. Most of the plasma was administered by enlisted Navy corpsmen.

The death rate was surprisingly low among the wounded, only 2.3 percent of those Marines did not recover. The credit for this low death rate has been given to the heroic doctors and corpsmen who worked at Tarawa. Credit also goes to plasma.

During this and previous South Pacific campaigns, corpsmen on duty with the Marines complained that their pouch for carrying medical supplies was too narrow and too deep. It was difficult for them to find what they were looking for in a hurry, and often they would have to remove the entire contents of the kit before locating the necessary item. Following Tarawa, a new pouch was developed and adopted. This one made all supplies accessible, with separate compartments for morphine syrettes and other small items.

On October 23, 1944, General Douglas MacArthur made a speech at a small ceremony in front of the Tacloban City Hall. "I have returned. By the grace of Almighty God our forces stand again on Philippine soil—soil consecrated in the blood of our two peoples...." But the fighting was far from over. General Yamashita, the Japanese commander in the Philippines, determined to make a stand on Leyte, sent a powerful force of 45,000 troops toward Ormoc. There were 250,000 soldiers on Luzon alone. The struggle for complete liberation of the Philippine Islands was a fierce and bloody one, and now Army medics found themselves in the same kind of war as their fellow Navy corpsmen. Rice paddies, filth, disease, heat and jungles . . . and the fanatic Japanese warrior.

Sergeant Major John Walker, now of the U.S. Army General Hospital and Medical Service Area, Frankfurt, Germany, was an aidman at Luzon. "There were four of us aidmen working as a team.... Things were pretty bad. I remember one time when there was a boy in the rice paddy beyond the line yelling for a medic. Four of us crawled out to get him. One aidman was hit, but the three of us kept going. We got him on a litter and hauled him back to the aid station, but by the time we got there, he was dead."

Walker wears the Bronze Star, the Army Commendation Medal and a Purple Heart for various actions at Dig-Dig in the Philippines. "I started out after a patient who was calling for me, but I couldn't get at him because of crossfire coming from a cave. I had three hand grenades with me so I threw them into the cave. Some of the shrapnel wounded me in the back. By this time the other boys could tell where the Jap enemy was holed up so they got after him with a flame thrower. I got my casualty out okay...."*

Many medics were not so fortunate as to survive the campaign in the Phillippines.

MEDAL OF HONOR (posthumous)

Technician Fourth Grade Laverne Parrish, twenty-seven years old, from Pablo, Montana, was medical aidman with Company C, 161st Infantry, during the fighting in Binalonan, Luzon, Philippine Islands, on January 18 and 24, 1945. On the 18th, he observed two wounded men under enemy fire and immediately went to their rescue. After moving one to cover, he crossed twenty-five yards of open ground to administer aid to the second man. In the early hours of the 24th, his company, crossing an open field near San Manuel, encountered intense enemy fire and was ordered to withdraw to the cover of a ditch. While treating the casualties, Technician Parrish observed two wounded still in the field. Without hesitation he left the ditch, crawled forward under enemy fire, and in two successive trips brought both men to safety.

He next administered aid to twelve casualties in the same field, crossing and recrossing the open area raked by hostile fire.

* From an interview with the author.

Making successive trips, he then brought three wounded in to cover.

After treating nearly all of the *thirty-seven* casualties suffered by his company, he was mortally wounded by mortar fire....

The war in the Pacific brought together the medics of the Army, Navy and Army Air Corps ashore, afloat and in the sky. Master Sergeant Gailen Allwood, now Chief Wardmaster at the Ninth Hospital Center in Heidelberg, Germany, was a graduate surgical flight technician in the Army Air Corps when he was assigned duty in the South Pacific flying C-47s and C-54s that had been fitted out for aeromedical evacuation. Sometimes he flew with the Navy, sometimes with the Marines. Wearing his Army uniform, he became known as the "dogface doc."

At Tarawa, the Navy PB2Y3 to which he was assigned landed on the water on D-day plus three. Navy corpsmen brought their patients to the docks, and together they loaded the men aboard the plane for the flight back to Hawaii. Because of the plane's configuration, litters had to be tilted and eased in sideways, but by stacking them in tiers, they were able to carry thirty-eight casualties in one load.

At Eniwetok, he was attached to the Marines. At Peleliu, there were twenty-five airplanes going in circles from the Admiralties to Guadalcanal, and back again for more. Aboard these planes were a pilot, a copilot and a medic. Nurses later flew in these South Pacific missions.

The flights were long and treacherous, and always over water. These medics knew that their chances for survival, should they be forced down in the Pacific, were slim. They carried no parachutes, only sidearms and Mae West life jackets. There were no markings on their planes, and had it not been for the Navy fighters who came out to escort their defenseless aircraft into the islands they would probably all have been shot down. The flights were exhausting. Allwood recorded 200 hours a month in flight time instead of the normal eighty in his two years of duty in that area. In all, he was involved in seven campaigns in the South Pacific.

One of the chief advantages of air evac was the comparative swiftness by which patients could be taken to hospitals. It was especially preferred for psychiatric patients, because on long ship voyages they had to be sedated for too long a time to be safe. Medics aboard air-evac planes devised special restraints from parachute rigging, so that patients' sedation could be kept at a minimum.

Flying alone with those disturbed, anxiety-ridden casualties required enormous endurance, patience, skill and understanding on the part of the med tech. For instance, on one flight in

World War II air evac following invasion of Iwo Jima, March 5, 1945, meant sharing the ride with cargo, but it was a means of getting the wounded to hospitals away from the front. *U.S. Navy Photo*

1944, Allwood had the full responsibility for a load of eighteen psychiatric patients, all the way from Australia to Hawaii, a trip lasting thirty hours. He didn't know his patients; he'd never seen them before. But he studied their charts to learn whether or not they were sedated, and if so how much sedation had been given.

They were all in restraints so that they could not harm themselves or others aboard, and the plane took off. Many of the patients were afraid to fly, let alone fly with restraints on their arms and legs, so Allwood did what he could to reassure them of their safety.

There was one stop at Port Moresby for refueling, and this is when Allwood served their chow. One by one, each patient was allowed an arm out of restraint in order to eat. Again the plane took off. During the entire trip, Gailen Allwood, a flying hospital staff of one, performed all the nursing and medical care for those helpless eighteen men in his charge.

In recognition of this heroic flight, Gailen Allwood became the first air-evac medic to be awarded the Air Medal.*

As the Allies battled their way across the Pacific, spending their blood for each inch of coral, so were the fighting troops clearing the Japanese out of northern Burma so that land communication with Nationalist China could be reestablished. The Burma Road was the lifeline for the Allies from hard-hit China to the outside countries, and men like General Stilwell, General Merrill and his Marauders, General Chennault, General Wingate and his Raiders all fought to smash the Mikado in the precarious terrain and steaming jungles of Burma.

The medical corps was divided into platoons, and it was their job to provide medical care to warriors fighting in scorching, dense, disease-infested jungles and harrowing mountainous terrain. Medics who traveled with Merrill's Marauders moved on foot, traveling light and fast. Their surgical teams were under

* From an interview with the author.

combat conditions all the time. Local anesthetics were their only pain killers; operations were performed on a ground sheet while the patient gritted his teeth. These patients were not green draftees, but tough, hand-picked volunteers of many nationalities: Indians, Chinese, British, Australians and Americans. Even so, they fell victim to malaria, typhus, skin infections and sores produced by ticks and leeches.

Medics serving in the China-Burma theater worked closely with the veterinarians because often the only way of transporting their food and medical supplies was on horses the size of Shetland ponies. Chinese communities in remote sectors usually organized litter-bearer teams. These teams, along with doctors and medics, carried the wounded up and down mountains, along narrow and hazardous trails, over high rocks and precipices to areas of safety on the west side of the Salween River in Burma. The trip by American surgical pack trains often lasted eight to ten days. Rocks and precipices often became slippery from the monsoon rains; horses would lose their footing and plunge hundreds of feet down the mountains. When this happened, medics climbed down to get the medical supplies and bring them back to the trail again. Once across the river, food supplies could be air dropped, but there were many medics who lived on nothing but rice for days at a time when weather prevented planes from coming over.

Medics served at small medical units set up at airfields throughout China. They accompanied casualties who were evacuated from airfield hospitals to base hospitals, then climbed aboard aircraft that flew them over the "hump" to the big base hospital in the Indian province of Assam.

SAIPAN—JUNE, 1944

Seven hundred miles northwest of the powerful Japanese base on the island of Truk and 1,000 miles northeast of another bristling base on Palau Island lay Saipan, the scene of one of the great battles of the Pacific. This stepping stone to Japan proper and vital supply point in the Marianas group was put under heavy bombardment by United States warships and bombing and strafing by carrier planes. When the Marines waded ashore there was little left but grotesque patches of torn jungle, jagged hills, soot, dust—and enemy Japanese.

Before going ashore, doctors aboard ship had seen to it that immunizations were up to date and that diseases and fungus were treated so they would not spread. Corpsmen had held constant consultations with one another, cramming all the time, trying to improve their knowledge so they would be ready when the time came. These corpsmen were all specialists; each knew his area of responsibility. One group, for instance, was assigned to pest control, others would go with the battalion up front and some corpsmen would be litter bearers.

The landing took place at night, but because the tide had turned, some men had to wade a long distance to shore. Some went in on ducks (amphibious trucks) and alligators (amphibious tanks). Corpsmen went right along with them.

Daylight showed the amazing sight of ships continuing their barrage. As flame throwers smoked out Japanese pillboxes, our carrier planes and ships bombed the heavier installations. There was sand, blood, wreckage and confusion everywhere. Black columns of smoke poured from gasoline dumps that had been fired. The men were dirty, sweaty and gray-colored, but by dawn had dug themselves into foxholes above the high-water mark. Chunks of clothing floated on the water. Many bodies had got caught on the bottoms of the amphibious vehicles. Coral dust covered everything, and still the shelling of the beach continued until the nerves of both officers and men were nearly at the breaking point.

Into this melee, medical units were landed in LVTs and LCTs. The first groups, composed of one medical officer and eight corpsmen from each troop carrier, were medical sections of the beach parties. They worked in highly exposed positions for as long as forty-eight hours at a time without rest. They gave emergency medical treatment and set up casualty evacuation centers in the sand even as the enemy strafed them. The battalion aid station acted as forward emergency and evacuation centers on the beaches.

From these stations, the company aidmen went out to administer first aid, constantly exposing themselves to enemy fire in order to reach the wounded. Their casualty rate was enormous, particularly in the first five days of the campaign. In the Fourth Marine Division alone, 161 medical officers and hospital corpsmen were killed because they could not protect themselves or seek cover from enemy fire. Their sacrifices were not in vain, for the most important factor in saving lives was the early transfusion of whole blood and plasma and the removal of casualties from the beaches to ships where lifesaving resuscitive measures could be taken.

During those first days of heavy fighting, one shore party evacuation station treated and evacuated 1,009 casualties during the period from D-day to D-day plus three. Ambulance jeeps, called "meat wagons," were often hit during air raids. Corpsmen who drove them unloaded their wounded during an attack, did what they could to protect them, then loaded them again and drove on. These young sailors worked at the front all day, then acted as litter bearers at night.

The 38th Field Hospital of the 27th Division was in Chinook village at the southern tip of the island. Surrounding the village was Bloody Ridge, from which the Japanese had recently been cleared. But snipers still remained behind to shoot at doctors, corpsmen and patients. There were slit trenches for patients to dive into during air raids, but doctors and corpsmen kept on operating during these raids, working by flashlight at night in the stifling blackout tent. Doctors wore shorts and masks because of the intense heat. Gowns were used only for major abdominal operations.

In the shock tent, everyone got plasma and some received up to five or six units. The doctor examined and prescribed, and the corpsmen went to work. Many of the casualties, more dead than alive, were so weak there was practically no pulse. But with care they miraculously returned to consciousness, asked for a cigarette and inquired about the fate of a buddy.

The Second Marine Division hospital was set up in a former Japanese radio building and was used for the less seriously wounded. Eight operating tables were in almost constant use. Disease and combat fatigue accounted for nearly one-third of the admissions.

On July 9, 1944, Admiral Chester W. Nimitz commander of all American Naval forces in the Pacific, said, "Our forces have completed the conquest of Saipan."

On July 25, Secretary of the Navy James V. Forrestal reported the casualties: 16,463. Of this total figure, 3,049 were killed in action, 13,049 wounded and 365 missing. Of the wounded, 5,000 had already been returned to action.

IWO JIMA—FEBRUARY, 1945

Although we had been bombing Japan since October 1944, we badly needed an emergency landing field for Superfortresses returning from Tokyo to the heavy bomber fields on Saipan. Iwo Jima, located about halfway between the enemy's capital and Saipan, would also enable us to provide P-51 fighter escorts for the bombers.

We knew that this tiny piece of volcanic real estate of seven and a half square miles would be defended to the death by 20,000 hardened troops, but it was hoped that we could soften them up in advance of the invasion. For two and a half months, planes of the Army, Navy and Marine Corps dropped 500-

pound bombs on the tiny island each day. Three days before the invasion, Task Force 52, which had taken part in the D-day landing at Normandy, shelled Iwo Jima.

The effect was nowhere near as deadly to the enemy as had been hoped. This was because the Japanese, mixing cement with volcanic ash from the extinct volcano of Mount Suribachi, had built a concrete honeycomb of interconnecting strongpoints. Their artillery, mortars and antitank guns were placed in steel-reinforced bunkers with walls four feet thick. Many of their underground tunnels were 800 yards long. Where natural caves had not obliged them with protection, they had hollowed out entire hills and wired them for electricity. Some of these underground "quarters" held up to 400 soldiers.

At 0900 on February 19, the Fourth and Fifth Marine Divisions, supported by the Fifth Fleet, began landing on the southeast shore of Iwo Jima. The Third Marine Division, held in reserve, landed on D-day plus two. Because of the terrain, the leathernecks were forced to make a frontal assault. This situation, the medical department had previously decided, would mean that twenty percent of the forces would be lost (of these, twenty-five percent killed, twenty-five percent returned to duty locally and fifty percent evacuated).

Much that had been learned in earlier campaigns was put into practice at Iwo. Prior to the operation, medical battalions were instructed to carry an additional 1,500 blankets, 5,000,000 units of gas gangrene antitoxin and 50,000,000 units of penicillin. Inspections were made, shortages were corrected and training of corpsmen in first aid, keeping of medical records, handling of litters and casualties in and out of boats was increased. At the close of their training session, corpsmen had been given a realistic practice drill of what they could expect in combat.

For the first time, whole blood was available from Distribution Center Number One at Guam. Prior to the Iwo Jima campaign, whole blood was obtained from corpsmen and Marines and occasionally from patients. Now it was flown via Naval Air Transport Service (NATS) to Hawaii, where it was de-iced, then on to Guam, where it was available for Iwo casualties.

Each medical company and division medical battalion had equipment for a 144-bed hospital, twice what was allotted for the Marianas campaign; thus there were approximately 3,592 beds available. The chain of evacuation of casualties included four LSTs specially equipped with medical personnel and supplies; they would "screen" and divide between hospital ships and transports. One LST was available for each of the invasion beaches, or two for each Marine division. Aboard each LST were four surgeons and twenty-seven corpsmen, increased on landing to five surgeons and thirty-five corpsmen. Two hospital ships and one APH would evacuate patients to Saipan and to Guam, where air-evac planes would fly them home as soon as possible.

In spite of such careful plans on the part of men whose job it was to save lives, Iwo Jima became the bloodiest battle in the history of the Marine Corps. Out of 60,000 men, 20,000 became casualties; 6,821 Americans died.

Strangely enough, all went well for the first hour. There were a few Japanese snipers here and there, but otherwise things were comparatively quiet. Company aidmen had debarked with their platoons, battalion aid-station personnel with the battalion command posts, and regimental aid-station men with the regimental command posts. Shore-party medical-party personnel in support of the battalion landing teams were debarked prior to H-hour. Four medical shore-party evacuation teams were landed between H-hour plus 30 and H-hour plus 120 minutes. Other division and corps medical units were landed as rapidly as the military situation permitted. Navy records state: "In the early phase of the assault, aid station personnel were separated into small groups and worked in shell craters or foxholes in the sand. . . ."

Navy corpsmen tend the wounded at an aid station on Iwo Jima. February 20, 1945. *U.S. Navy Photo*

What does this mean? What happened during those terrible hours, days, weeks on that tiny Pacific island?

That first day 30,000 Marines struggled ashore only to have their guns, tanks, DUKWs and amphibious half-tracks become stuck in the volcanic sand. Leathernecks sank to their knees as they tried to walk, and then suddenly the whole island seemed to explode in gunfire. The ground was strewn with thousands of lethal mines. Harmless mounds became tops of concrete pillboxes. Even brush piles concealed Japanese pillboxes, each of which had to be put out of action by flame throwers and dynamite.

In spite of training, planning and experience, Navy corpsmen assigned to the assault companies took the most tragic beating in their history. And nothing seemed to work as planned.

Typical of the problems confronting corpsmen occurred when twenty-six of them came ashore in the sixth wave of troops. Their chief pharmacist's mate was shot in the jaw as he stepped off the landing craft. He was immediately returned to the hospital ship. The medical party, carrying seabags filled with medical supplies, pushed inland some seventy-five yards and picked a spot for their station in an antitank ditch. Some had left their bags on the beach, but when they returned to get them, bomb bursts had split most of them wide open, destroying boxes of valuable plasma. The worst blow came when the boat carrying their litters was sunk.

It was impossible to stand erect on the beach, so corpsmen crawled from casualty to casualty to bandage wounds, administer morphine and plasma. Wounded men were lying all around.

Within an hour after the aid station was set up, a shell exploded on one side and fragments injured several of the men. The medical officer realized that the revetment, though appearing to offer good protection for an aid station, was a logical target for the Japanese guns. He ordered the men to pack up equipment and move to a large bomb crater, where medical personnel continued their work.

By nightfall, eleven corpsmen were dead. That night a Navy shore party transferring wounded men to a ship suffered a direct hit. All twenty-five men were lost. Now, since boats could not get through, corpsmen set up their own system by digging foxholes for their wounded. Finally the Navy turned the LST anchored 400 yards offshore into operating rooms, using officers' living quarters as wards and wardroom tables as operating tables. By late afternoon the next day, 1,500 men had been treated on the LST's floating sick bay.

On the beach, a Marine who had been blinded and had both hands blown off was groping his way toward the shoreline when a corpsman saw him and ran a gantlet of fire to get him to safety.

A corpsman in battle for the first time sewed up four chest wounds under fire and undoubtedly helped save the lives of the four injured men.

A corpsman crawled to the aid of Captain Dwayne E. "Bobo" Mears, who had been shot through the neck and was in shock from the loss of blood. He buried the lower part of the captain's body in sand so that he would offer a smaller target for the Japanese riflemen. It helped, but the captain died later aboard a hospital ship.

Navy corpsmen bled and died at Iwo Jima and the Marine Corps will not forget their sacrifice. In the Fourth Marine Division alone, the casualty rate among these noncombatants was thirty-eight percent.

Usually battles are overshadowed by succeeding events in history. This is not true with the amphibious epic at Iwo Jima. It was on D-day plus one that the 28th Marine Regiment jumped off for Mount Suribachi from where a deadly rain of fire was coming. Concealed pillboxes were everywhere, and each had to be put out by flame throwers and dynamite. By the end of the day they had advanced only 200 yards. Twenty-nine Marines were dead and 113 wounded. The next day, after a forty-plane strike, they started out again and by nightfall reached the base of the mountain. There were no trails up the steep side, so it was a matter of climbing hand over hand, past caves concealing desperate enemy troops. On D-day plus three, the rains came, turning the volcanic ash to muck. Guns jammed but still there were fierce enemy troops all around them. On D-day plus four a few Marines finally reached the top, where they found a length of pipe on which they could raise a small American flag they carried with them. But the flag was too small to be seen from the beach. Several Marines scrambled down the mountainside, borrowed a huge flag and carried it back up to the top.

Pharmacist's Mate Second Class John H. Bradley helped raise the American flag on Mount Suribachi, Iwo Jima, February 23, 1945, in the bloodiest campaign in Marine Corps history. *U.S. Marine Corps Photo, courtesy, Associated Press*

Pharmacist's Mate
First Class Francis J. Pierce

President Harry S. Truman presents the Medal of Honor to George
E. Wahlen, HM2, USNR, during the Nimitz Day ceremony at the White
House. October 5, 1945. *U.S. Navy Photo*

The photograph of this flag raising, taken by Associated Press correspondent Joe Rosenthal, became the most famous of all World War II photos. Three of the six men were later killed in the battle. Another died after the war. The second man from the right of the picture is John H. Bradley, Pharmacist's Mate Second Class. He is now in the furniture business in Wisconsin.

MEDAL OF HONOR

Francis J. Pierce, Pharmacist's Mate First Class, USN, was twenty-one years old at the time he was attached to the Second Battalion, 24th Marines, Fourth Marine Division, during the Iwo Jima campaign, March 15 and 16, 1945. Almost continuously under fire while carrying out the most dangerous volunteer assignments, Pierce gained valuable knowledge of the terrain and disposition of troops. Caught in heavy enemy rifle and machine-gun fire which wounded a corpsman and two of the eight stretcher bearers who were carrying two wounded Marines to a forward aid station on March 15, Pierce quickly took charge of the party, carried the newly wounded men to a sheltered position, and rendered first aid. After directing the evacuation of three of the casualties, he stood upright in the open to draw the enemy's fire and, with his weapon blasting, enabled the litter bearers to reach cover. Turning his attention to the other two casualties, he was attempting to stop the profuse bleeding of one man when a Japanese fired from a cave less than twenty yards away and wounded his patient again. Risking his own life to save his patient, Pierce deliberately exposed himself to draw the attacker from the cave and destroyed him with the last of his ammunition. Then lifting the wounded man to his back, he advanced unarmed through deadly rifle fire across 200 feet of open terrain. Despite exhaustion and in the face of warnings against such a suicidal mission, he again traversed the same fireswept path to rescue the remaining Marine. On the following morning, he led a combat patrol to the sniper nest and while aiding a stricken Marine, was seriously wounded. Refusing aid for himself, he directed treatment for the casualty, at the same time maintaining protective fire for his comrades. Completely fearless, completely devoted to the care of his patients, Pierce inspired the entire battalion. His valor in the face of extreme peril sustains and enhances the finest traditions of the United States Naval Service.

MEDAL OF HONOR

George Edward Wahlen, Pharmacist's Mate Second Class, USN, twenty-one years old, served with the Second Battalion, 26th Marines, Fifth Marine Division, during action against enemy Japanese forces on Iwo Jima on March 3, 1945. Painfully wounded in the bitter action on February 26, Wahlen remained on the battlefield, advancing well forward of the front lines to aid a wounded Marine and carrying him back to safety despite a terrific concentration of fire. Tireless in his ministrations, he consistently disregarded all danger to attend his fighting comrades as they fell under the devastating rain of shrapnel and bullets, and rendered prompt assistance to various elements of his combat group as required. When an adjacent platoon suffered heavy casualties, he defied the continuous pounding of heavy mortars and deadly fire of enemy rifles to care for the wounded, working rapidly in an area swept by constant fire and treating fourteen casualties before returning to his own platoon. Wounded again on March 2, he gallantly refused evacuation, moving out with his company the following day in a furious assault across 600 yards of open terrain and repeatedly rendering medical aid while exposed to the blasting fury of powerful Japanese guns. Stout-hearted and indomitable, he persevered in his determined efforts as his unit waged fierce battle and, unable to walk after sustaining a third agonizing wound, resolutely crawled fifty yards to administer first aid to still another fallen fighter. By his dauntless fortitude and valor, Wahlen served as a constant inspiration and contributed vitally to the high morale of his company during this strategically important engagement.

MEDAL OF HONOR (posthumous)

Jack Williams, Pharmacist's Mate Third Class, USNR, was serving with the Third Battalion, 28th Marines, Fifth Marine Division during the occupation of Iwo Jima, March 3, 1945. Gallantly going forward of the front lines under intense enemy small-arms fire to assist a Marine wounded in a fierce grenade battle, Williams dragged the man to a shallow depression and was kneeling, using his own body as a screen from the sustained fire as he administered first aid, when struck in the abdomen and groin three times by hostile rifle fire. Momentarily stunned, he quickly recovered and completed his ministrations before applying battle dressings to his own multiple wounds. Unmindful of his own urgent need for medical attention, he remained in the perilous fireswept area to care for another Marine casualty. Heroically completing his task despite pain and profuse bleeding, he then endeavored to make his way to the rear in search of adequate aid for himself when struck down by a Japanese sniper bullet, which caused his collapse. Succumbing later as a result of his self-sacrificing service to others, Williams by his courageous determination, unwavering fortitude and valiant performance of duty, served as an inspiring example of heroism, in keeping with the highest traditions of the United States Naval Service. He gallantly gave his life for his country.

Pharmacist's Mate
First Class John H. Willis

Hospital Apprentice
First Class Fred F. Lester

Pharmacist's Mate
Second Class William David Halyburton

Pharmacist's Mate
Third Class Jack Williams

MEDAL OF HONOR (posthumous)

John Harlan Willis, Pharmacist's Mate First Class, USN, served as a platoon corpsman with the Third Battalion, 27th Marines, Fifth Marine Division, during operations against enemy Japanese forces on Iwo Jima, February 29, 1945. Constantly imperiled by artillery and mortar fire from strong and mutually supporting pillboxes and caves studding Hill 362 in the enemy's cross-island defenses, Willis resolutely administered first aid to the many Marines wounded during the furious close-in fighting until he himself was struck by shrapnel and was ordered back to the battle aid station. Without waiting for official medical release, he quickly returned to his company and, during a savage hand-to-hand enemy counterattack, daringly advanced to the extreme front lines under mortar and sniper fire to aid a Marine lying wounded in a shell hole. Completely unmindful of his own danger as the Japanese intensified their attack, Willis calmly continued to administer blood plasma to his patient, promptly returning the first hostile grenade which landed in the shell hole while he was working, and hurling back seven more in quick succession before the ninth one exploded in his hand and instantly killed him. By his great personal valor in saving others at the sacrifice of his own life, he inspired his companions, although terrifically outnumbered, to launch a fiercely determined attack and repulse the enemy force....

By March 26, 1945, the battle for Iwo Jima was over. The terrible sacrifices of the American fighting men were not in vain because before the war's end, Iwo was to provide emergency landing for 2,251 planes, or a saving of 25,000 pilots and crew members who otherwise might have perished in the Pacific.

A little over a month later, American forces moved in on Okinawa, another small island in the Ryukyus just 350 miles south of Japan. This was to be used as a final staging area for the invasion of Japan proper. A naval and air base there would bring major industrial cities of Japan within close bombing range. From a medical point of view, Okinawa was significant because practically every disease known in Japan was found there. Had the military forces been called upon to invade Japan, this knowledge would have been invaluable.

By now, the empire of Japan was on its knees. But its fighting men would make a last-ditch stand. They planned to use 350 suicide boats loaded with high explosives against the invasion fleet. They would also use their Kamikaze planes.

Before the battle was finished, the Japanese had lost 117,000 men and 7,830 airplanes. American losses: 49,000 casualties, including 12,520 killed in action. Losses would have been much greater had not the medical department been so well seasoned and prepared. And by this time, corpsmen had become experts in improvisation and invention. Chief Pharmacist's Mate John A. Gallegher, USNR, remembered the campaign in Tulagi when corpsmen, unable to use rigid stretchers to carry wounded Marines over cliff-studded terrain, were forced to use ponchos instead. In Okinawa, Gallegher devised a stretcher weighing four pounds, six ounces that could be compressed into a small pack and attached to the cartridge belt. If rigidity were preferred, poles could be inserted into its lengthwise seams. Three overlapping straps secured the patient in the lying position while two other straps could be fastened around the thighs, similar to the way in which a parachute harness is applied. It could be carried by from one to six men, used rigid or otherwise and could be lowered by rope with the patient fully secure.

This stretcher, along with dozens of other on-the-spot inventions, saved many lives. But in the process of aiding their fallen comrades, many corpsmen were killed.

MEDAL OF HONOR

Robert Eugene Bush, Hospital Apprentice First Class, USN, was nineteen years old when he served as medical corpsman with a Rifle Company, Second Battalion, Fifth Marine Division, in action against enemy Japanese forces on Okinawa Jima, Ryukyu Islands, May 2, 1945. Fearlessly braving the fury of artillery, mortar and machine-gun fire from strongly entrenched hostile positions, Bush constantly and unhesitatingly moved from one casualty to another to attend the wounded falling under the enemy's murderous barrages. As the attack passed over a ridge top, Bush was advancing to administer blood plasma to a Marine officer lying wounded on the skyline when the Japanese launched a savage counterattack. In this perilously exposed position, he resolutely maintained the flow of life-giving plasma. With bottle held high in one hand, Bush drew his pistol with the other and fired into the enemy's ranks until his ammunition was expended. Quickly seizing a discarded carbine, he trained his fire on the Japanese charging point-blank over the hill, accounting for six of the enemy despite his serious wounds and the loss of one eye suffered during his desperate battle in defense of the helpless man. With the hostile force finally routed, he calmly disregarded his own critical condition to complete his mission, valiantly refusing medical treatment for himself until his officer patient had been evacuated, and collapsing only after attempting to walk to the battle aid station.

MEDAL OF HONOR (posthumous)

Fred Faulkner Lester, Hospital Apprentice First Class, USN, nineteen years old, served as medical corpsman with an assault rifle platoon, attached to the First Battalion, 22d Marines, Sixth

Marine Division, during action against enemy Japanese forces on Okinawa Jima in the Ryukyu chain, June 8, 1945. Quick to spot a wounded Marine lying in an open field beyond the front lines following the relentless assault against a strategic Japanese hill position, Lester unhesitatingly crawled toward the casualty under a concentrated barrage from hostile machine guns, rifles and grenades. Torn by enemy rifle bullets as he inched forward, he stoically disregarded the mounting fury of Japanese fire and his own pain to pull the wounded man toward a covered position. Struck by enemy fire a second time before he reached cover, he exerted tremendous effort and succeeded in pulling his comrade to safety where, too seriously wounded himself to administer aid, he instructed two of his squad in proper medical treatment of the rescued Marine. Realizing that his own wounds were fatal, he staunchly refused medical attention for himself and, gathering his fast-waning strength with calm determination, coolly and expertly directed his men in the treatment of two other wounded Marines, succumbing shortly thereafter.

MEDAL OF HONOR (posthumous)

William David Halyburton, Pharmacist's Mate Second Class, USN, served as a corpsman with a Marine rifle company in the Second Battalion, Fifth Marines, First Marine Division during action against enemy Japanese forces on Okinawa Jima in the Ryukyu chain, May 19, 1945. Undaunted by the deadly accuracy of Japanese counterfire as his unit pushed the attack through a strategically important draw, Halyburton unhesitatingly dashed across the draw and up the hill into an open, fireswept field where the company advance squad was suddenly pinned down under a terrific concentration of mortar, machine-gun and sniper fire with resultant severe casualties. Moving steadily forward despite the enemy's merciless barrage, he reached the wounded Marine who lay farthest away and was rendering first aid when his patient was struck for the second time by a Japanese bullet. Instantly placing himself in the direct line of fire, he shielded the fallen fighter with his own body and staunchly continued his ministrations although constantly menaced by the slashing fury of shrapnel and bullets falling on all sides. Alert, determined and completely unselfish in his concern for the helpless Marine, he persevered in his efforts until he himself sustained mortal wounds and collapsed, heroically sacrificing himself that his comrade might live.

8

Training and Specialization

AT the close of World War II, thousands of medics returned to their peacetime occupations. Those who remained in the service became career men, and in many instances their jobs became that of administrating and training young men entering the corps. A highly important advance came in August 1947 when the Eightieth Congress approved the establishment of the Medical Service Corps. It provides for a commissioned rank structure from second lieutenant through colonel in the Army and ensign to captain in the Navy. It consists of four sections: the Medical Allied Science Section for those holding degrees in sciences allied to medicine; the Sanitary Engineering Section for those with degrees in sanitation and environmental engineering; the Optometry Section for those holding degrees from schools of optometry; and the Pharmacy, Supply, and Administration Section for those with degrees in pharmacy, business administration, hospital administration, supply, procurement, public relations and a score of other services necessary to the operation of the medical services of the armed forces. Many former medics and corpsmen fit into this section.

In September 1966, Congress approved a bill authorizing one

officer of the Army Medical Service Corps to hold the rank of brigadier general. Also approved and sent to the White House was a bill to authorize the commissioning of males in the Army and Navy Nurse and Medical Specialists Corps. These positions were formerly open only to reservists and women. The Air Force, needing more MSC senior officers, is requesting approval for twenty-six additional colonels and eighty-six additional lieutenant colonels.

There have been many changes in the selection and training of the Army medical soldier since World War II. Now, for instance, he must take an aptitude test in order to qualify and be selected for the ten-week medical training course at Fort Sam Houston in San Antonio, Texas. And he can no longer be just a "conscientious objector" (such as actor Lew Ayres, a medic during World War II) with no training in infantry tactics, physical conditioning and defense against gas attacks. Today, all conscientious objectors are sent to Fort Sam Houston for medical training. There were about 800 last year.

Now, everyone enlisted or drafted into the Army must have eight weeks of basic training in soldiering. From "basic," the young soldier can be selected to go to Fort Sam Houston, where he will be further schooled as a medical soldier. On graduation, he is classified as an MOS (Military Occupation Specialty) 91A, which qualifies him to be a medical corpsman, aidman, platoon or company ambulance driver, orderly or litter bearer. He is then assigned to units to perform a myriad of tasks: basic first aid, transportation of patients, all emergency medical procedures, hospital care, preventive medicine, field sanitation and training soldiers in the medical aspects of survival. From a 91A the medical soldier can apply for forty weeks of further training at any of the Army's seven advanced medical specialists schools. The instructors are nurses, enlisted teachers and advanced medical specialists. The clinical specialist's MOS code is 91C. The 91C qualifies him as a practical nurse.

Ideally, the Army would take only qualified volunteers for medical training, but this cannot be depended upon. There are a fair number of boys volunteering who have had college training, and they, of course, are eagerly trained and assigned to responsible jobs by the Army Medical Service. But plenty of jobs that are absolutely necessary do not require a brilliant mind. In general, the Army has designated skill levels, and a man can go as high in rank as his skill level indicates.

The Army's peacetime medic has a wide variety of jobs. A significant "behind the scenes" service they provide their fellow servicemen as well as the worldwide civilian population is in the field of preventive medicine. Medics with the United States Army in Europe (USAREUR) are sanitation inspectors of food service. Although all their work is done under supervision, they do the actual legwork on epidemiological studies. If a food-poisoning incident occurs, medics will take the patients' histories as to what was eaten, at what time—and where. They collect water samples, which they deliver to the laboratory to see if the water is safe for troops to drink. They interview patients with venereal disease, list the names of contacts and report this information to local authorities. In industrial hygiene, medics check motor pools to see if the carbon-monoxide level is low enough to provide a safe and healthy environment for the workers. Army medics are active in rodent and insect control. They collect specimens and identify them. They assist in studies of insecticides to determine which insects are resistant to DDT.

Some units in the NATO countries have no medical support other than what is sent to them. Here is where the traveling dental van and immunization teams provide important services. Although there is always a medical doctor available, enlisted medics are the ones who give the shots.

Wherever troops of the United States Army are sent, their medics go right along with them. They work in 83 hospitals spread around the world, 300 dispensaries and 300 separate dental clinics. Since World War II, the Army Medical Service has replaced twenty hospitals in the United States; three others are under construction, two others are funded and under design and eleven others require replacement.

As the soldier of yesterday has become a highly specialized, intensively trained fighter, so has the Army medic become an expert in his chosen field. There are many male nurses who parachute out of airplanes with the 101st and 82d Airborne Divisions. The Special Forces aidman is as new as the next wonder drug. He is not only trained in his own specialty as a medic, but also is cross-trained in at least two other skills. Before he even begins his twelve weeks of Special Forces training at Fort Bragg, he must have thirty-five weeks of training at Brooke Army Medical Center, Fort Sam Houston, in Texas. Later he goes to work at Fort Bragg, where he learns to perform minor surgery if necessary, treat gunshot wounds and compound fractures. He is well schooled in tropical diseases. His aid kit is more elaborate than those of other medics because he must be prepared to teach medical skills to guerrilla medics of the host country. The Special Forces medic is trained in jungle and mountain warfare, underwater demolition, psychological warfare, and foreign language. And he is a qualified military parachutist.

The dozens of specialties taught to medics are not only valuable during their military careers but also serve them well in the civilian world. Many men return to school when their Army tour is finished. They find themselves way ahead of the class working toward an M.D. or other science degree. Others who seek jobs similar to the ones they held as Army medics find their skills in great demand. An Army-trained medical records clerk can later work in a civilian hospital as a receiving clerk or medical records librarian. A clinical-psychology specialist can work for industry as a personnel psychologist or a psychologist for the physically handicapped. An Army medic who is a social-work specialist can find employment as an occupational case aide. Physical-therapy specialists are in great demand as civilian electrotherapists, hydrotherapists, masseurs and physical therapists. The Army's reconditioning specialists can become athletic coaches, instructors in physical education and recreation therapists. Electrocardiograph/basal-metabolism-rate specialists who are properly trained can later work as electrocardiograph technicians.

Among the Army medics, everyone who has the ability and drive for hard work has a chance to get ahead. SP-7 Roberto Barrera, whose ancestry is Spanish, enlisted in his hometown of Brownsville, Texas, when he was eighteen years old. After his basic training he went to work in the medical depot in Japan during the Korean conflict. Later he took the medical specialist advanced course at Fort Sam Houston. He now works as a practical nurse, at the Army Hospital in Frankfurt, Germany, is licensed in Oklahoma, but plans to stay in the Army until he retires. He likes to work with people, is patient and kind and can often get smiling cooperation from cases with reputations for being "impossible." He loves working in the obstetric and pediatric wards because he is a softie for babies and small children. But the surgical ward is his favorite. "There," he says, "you can really learn. It's like working with a car . . . breaking it down to see what makes it tick. It's so interesting all the time."

Lee Luna, who is Chief of Histopathology Laboratories at the Armed Forces Institute of Pathology at the Walter Reed Army Medical Center, Washington, D.C., is another example of how medics make the most of their opportunities. Lee, of Mexican descent, grew up on a small farm in Colorado. When Lee was a young child, his father, hearing of serious illness in his family, crossed the border into Mexico for a visit. He apparently was unable to return to Colorado, and Lee never saw him again. Life was very hard for the Luna family.

Lee enlisted in the Army in 1947 and took his basic training at Fort Lewis in Washington State. Following this was the job at Madigan Hospital, where he was on "steady KP." He was then sent to Washington, D.C., where he was assigned to the old Institute of Pathology at Seventh Street and Independence Avenue. "I was told to clean up the lab—and to be a general handyman." A step up in his career came when his supervisor gave him the job of sharpening knives, the sort used for cutting tissues for study under the microscopes. "I spent thirty days sharpening the same kind of knife, hour after hour." The supervisor liked his work and his spirit, and Lee was given other knives to sharpen. Soon, his rating was changed to that of medical technician.

In the fall of 1951, Lee Luna was sent to Korea with the 8217 Medical Field Laboratory. "I worked seven days a week, 12 to 15 hours a day performing autopsies, parasitology, chemistries, bacteriology. There were thirty people in our outfit, including the officers, and I was made NCOIC [noncommissioned officer in charge] of the labs. We set them up in bombed-out buildings, tents or in makeshift buildings on the compound of the hospital."

Did he study much on his own?

"I read everything I could lay my hands on. I studied every spare minute."

Lee Luna spent six years in the Army, and he says he owes everything to his military service. "It irks me to hear people say the Army ruins boys. This just isn't so."

As a civilian, Lee Luna returned to the Armed Forces Institute of Pathology to work as a technician. The Institute was reorganized in 1954, with the creation of seven sections, one of which was placed in his charge. In 1960, he became Chief of the Laboratories. Today, he is recognized as an outstanding leader in his field. He frequently publishes papers in such journals as *American Society of Medical Technology* on the subject of histopathology techniques and staining, for which he has developed new techniques. He is also in charge of a teaching program at the AFIP. Three times a year he gives a course of ten two-hour classes to Army and Air Force personnel. One hour is devoted to lecture and the other to microscopic demonstration.

Lee Luna's career did indeed take him a long way from that small farm in Colorado.

The Navy corpsmen of the late 30's and World War II were a remarkable breed of well-trained, highly motivated career men. In those days there was usually a better rotation between ship and shore duty than there was in other specialties of the Navy. A greater prize went to the corpsman generalist who knew hospital and nursing procedures, first aid, operating-room techniques, ambulance driving, administrative and accounting office work, and food management. All these jobs could be handled without direct supervision by the medical officer. Corpsmen who made first class were eligible for "independent duty," serving without a doctor aboard. They were not required to be a real expert but rather to have a good knowledge of all these fields.

Corpsmen today are different. They are specialists in optical, dental, X-ray, pharmacy, bacteriology, medical records, medical photography, psychiatry, and the whole spectrum of medical care, the prevention and treatment of disease. Even the corpsman who works in the operating room must be extensively trained for such procedures as are required for, say, open-heart surgery. Today's boys are not inhibited because of economics. They are not worried about a depression so they are more free to choose specialties and seek further training. But in spite of the differences between the new and the old breed, the tradition and spirit of the early corpsman still holds true. His willingness to learn and serve is as fresh and exciting as ever. It is often a surprise, a real phenomenon, to people who have never before seen corpsmen go into action when the need arises.

Vice Admiral Robert B. Brown, MC, USN, Surgeon General of the Navy, never ceases to wonder at the sincere devotion to duty of corpsmen he had observed through the years. "I've seen corpsmen volunteer for extra watches instead of taking liberty because of their concern for a sick youngster on their ward. And mind you, these are not rare instances. This type of thing happens often. Corpsmen somehow develop an empathy with their patients that is absolutely wonderful. I have heard so many comments and of course there are files of letters from patients, many of whom are VIPs, who express their initial surprise and certainly their gratitude for the care given them by these young corpsmen."

Admiral Brown feels strongly about the sometimes popular belief that the youth of this nation is not what it used to be, that the qualities of honesty, devotion and eagerness to be of service have somehow disappeared from the current scene. "Being a corpsman in the United States Navy gives these young people a chance to do something really important. It brings out the good in them. Their energies are channeled in the right direction. There is nothing wrong with our youth that a really important tour of service to his fellow man cannot rectify....

"It is important to note that when we refer to doctors and nurses who have had years of professional training and who have long ago decided that this is what they want to do with their lives, we are talking about an entirely different set of circumstances. The average enlisted corpsman is a youngster who is swept up in his obligation to do military service. He not only has the abrupt changeover from civilian life to that of the military, but he is thrust into an environment of medicine and science which in many instances is equally bewildering.

"There is no adequate way to express the pride and appreciation that we in the military, and for that matter, the nation, have for the men of the United States Navy Hospital Corps."*

* From an interview with the author.

Of course, good Navy corpsmen don't "just happen." As with the Army, all Navy recruits must complete their basic, or "boot camp," training. From there, they go on to hospital corps training. Each week during the year, classes are formed at Corpsmen "A" schools located at San Diego, California, and Great Lakes Naval Training Center in Illinois. Courses at these identical schools last for sixteen weeks, and they are designed to teach basic nursing and patient care to corpsmen and corps Waves. The Navy Bureau of Personnel sets up quotas for Class "A" schools in line with the current military needs. Some years the quota may be 4,000; other years it is many more.

The Hospital Corps schools are under the control of the Bureau of Medicine and Surgery with the local commanding officer providing the immediate supervision. About ninety percent of the students are men new to the Navy who have just completed boot camp. The other ten percent are "strikers," men who have had duty with the fleet but who have shown interest and qualification for training as corpsmen.

The basic course is a tough one, but because of the responsibilities these young men may have to face, it is necessary to cram all possible knowledge and skill into it. Seventy-five hours are spent on anatomy and physiology where the student is given an elementary description of the structure and function of the human body. During this time, he learns the basic biological processes, definitions and the organic structure of cells and tissue. He is introduced to medical nomenclature and is familiarized with the location and function of the many studies and components of the human anatomy.

There are 60 hours spent on materia medica and toxicology, 33 hours on hygiene and sanitation, and 25 hours on metrology, review of decimals, addition, subtraction, multiplication, division, converting decimals to fractions, etc. There are 25 hours devoted to atomic, biological and chemical warfare defense, 62 hours on military subjects such as those taught at Naval stations and aboard ship the world over. A time-consuming class in the "A" schools is the 120 hours spent on first aid and minor surgery. Another is the 240 hours in the class of principles and techniques of patient care.

When the corpsman graduates from this course, he is sent to a dispensary, a Naval hospital, a ship or other duty station and continues his on-the-job training. After a while, he may get orders to an advanced school, of which there are about thirty. These schools, located at Naval hospitals, train corpsmen to serve all the needs in the Naval service, from optician to submarine medicine, as well as related civilian fields. They also equip corpsmen for accreditation by civilian educational institutions. For instance, at the United States Naval Medical School located at the National Naval Medical Center, Bethesda, Maryland, postgraduate instruction is available for medical officers and hospital corpsmen. There are twelve special technical schools for enlisted men, including pharmacy, chemistry, laboratory procedures, X-ray and photofluorography, medical photography, physical medicine, occupational therapy, radioactive isotopes, duplicating techniques, tissue bank, blood bank and optometry.

The school for corpsmen at the Portsmouth Naval Hospital in Virginia is the oldest one of its kind in the Navy. Its Chief of Enlisted Training Service is Commander M. W. Coggburn, MSC, USN, one of five brothers who served with the Navy in World War II. Only one of the brothers left the Navy after the war. He became a doctor.

Commander Coggburn served all over the Pacific as a corpsman and received his commission as a Medical Service Corps officer in 1953. He knows how to run a school for enlisted corpsmen because he has had so many years' experience in both peace and war. And he remembers the days when he worked

The Hospital Corps school at Portsmouth, Virginia, is open to graduates of Class "A" schools. The proficiency and knowledge that these young corpsmen gain here will mean the difference between life and death to many people. *U.S. Navy Photo*

fifty to sixty hours a week, but ". . . corpsmen don't have to work such long hours anymore. . . ." The school at Portsmouth is open to men who have graduated from the Class "A" schools.*

The Enlisted Training Service under Commander Coggburn's command teaches three classes: (1) MAT, the Medical Administrative Technicians. Men who enter this class are senior, second-class petty officers and above. Normally, they have ten to fifteen years' service and they consider this their lifetime career. They seldom drop out of this thirty-week course. (2) Advanced Hospital Corps Technique. This is for second- and first-class corpsmen. It is a twenty-week course in preparation for independent duty. (3) Pharmacy School. This thirty-two-week course is open to corpsmen of lower ratings, HM3, and

---

* From an interview with the author.

some HM2's. The men in this class are young, eighteen, nineteen, and twenty years old, who have had very little training and experience outside their Class "A" school. They may have had some previous on-the-job training. The attrition rate is about two or three out of a class of twenty-five or thirty students. In this important school, all the techniques of pharmacy are taught. Accuracy and skill are vital because these men are actually mixing drugs and prescriptions that could cure or kill someone.

The school is also involved with the corpsmen serving at the Naval Hospital in Portsmouth. Two hours each week, corpsmen attend the school in preparation for advancement. This system also keeps them abreast of new and different techniques and exposes them to many areas of work.

There are twenty-nine chief petty officers teaching at the school. They are all graduates of the Instructor's School.

Corpsmen have a tremendous amount of knowledge when they leave the Portsmouth school. Interns after four years of medical school have said that the exams for graduation would be difficult for them to pass, but the corpsmen get through.

Another important specialization field for graduates of Class "A" schools is the Field Medical Service School. This is in preparation for duty with the Fleet Marine Force. About ten percent of the Navy's corpsmen serve with the Marine Corps in peacetime. The number is considerably higher in time of war.

The four-week course, held at Camp Pendleton, California, and Camp Lejeune, North Carolina, is designed to teach the corpsman what he will face when serving with the Marines. The curriculum includes organization of the medical department, concepts of amphibious operations and duties of medical units, survival methods under battle conditions, first aid on the battlefield and patient evacuation.

When he enters the school, the corpsman is given his 782 gear, including a rifle, pack, utility clothing and all other equipment that a Marine uses. This, except for his rating badge, makes him identical to other Marines. In addition to his Marine equipment, the corpsman carries his first-aid pack.

For four weeks, the field corpsman learns how to be a Marine and how to adapt his previous medical training to a field-type situation. In short, he learns how to keep himself alive so that he can save the lives of others.

Wearing his "utilities" in battle training, he crawls forward on his stomach while bursts of thirty-caliber machine guns send slugs whistling past and exploding charges of TNT light up a night sky. He learns how to use a rifle and what it's like to make an assault on a fortified position. The corpsman is taught the use of communications and the procedure with field phones, close-order drill, military formations, Marine Corps history and traditions, security, defensive tactics and combat patrols. The Marines accept him as one of their own, for the corpsman shares all the responsibilities, the dangers and the rough life in the field, just so that he can look after them when needed.

Another important school for Navy corpsmen is the Preventive Medicine Technicians School, established in November 1950 at the Oakland Naval Hospital. Here, a select group of hospital corpsmen from second class to chief receive twenty-two weeks of comprehensive training in all phases of sanitation science. Included in this science are inspection, storage and laboratory examination of food; inspection of water supply, including swimming pools; proper methods of disposal of garbage, refuse and human wastes; identification and control of insects and rodents. Corpsmen also learn how to survey living spaces in order to determine if lighting, ventilation and sanitary facilities meet the accepted Navy standards. They learn to check plumbing for cross connections and back siphonage, compile and evaluate medical statistics, survey working spaces to detect industrial hazards, inspect barber shops and speak publicly to others about their findings. These corpsmen, sometimes called "Flashlight Charley" or "rat catcher," also conduct a Food Sanitation Training Program and hold general sanitation and venereal-disease control classes.

Courses ranging from one to twelve months are taught at various Naval hospitals equipped for such specialized work as aviation medicine, blood bank, bone bank, chemistry, clinical laboratory, electrocardiography, electroencephalography, medical administration, medical duplicating, medical-equipment repair, medical photography, medical research, neuropsychiatry, occupational therapy, operating-room procedures, optometric fabrication, orthopedic appliances, pharmacy, physical therapy, submarine medicine, urology and X-ray. Corpsmen are also trained in embalming techniques, medical-equipment maintenance and sound-motion-picture techniques in armed forces activities.

Corpsmen are trained in medical deep-sea diving, because no Navy diving gang will operate without their corpsman close at hand. Diving gangs of eight to twelve men work aboard submarine rescue vessels and salvage ships. Although the corpsman wears the same deep-sea diving suit and hard hat to work alongside other divers in the murky depths, his primary and independent duty mission is medical.

Before World War II there were fewer than six diving corpsmen in the Navy. Now, there are about seventy to take care of the 450 first-class divers and others in the fleet. And to be a first-class diving corpsman is a very special thing.

In order to be eligible for the twenty-six-week course at the Navy's Deep Sea Diving School, home-ported on the Potomac River at Washington, D.C., a corpsman must be a graduate of boot camp and have a rating of E4 or above. The corpsman would be a graduate of a Class "A" Hospital Corps school and would have had some on-the-job training before applying to this school, which is the only one in the entire Navy that can graduate a first-class diver. A second-class diver, because of his limited experience, can dive only to a depth of 150 feet. A first-class diver is limited, operationally, to 365 feet, but this is extending all the time. He is trained to use a mixture of helium and oxygen for his breathing when working in very deep water. On graduation, he is a highly skilled, meticulously trained pro; his responsibility for his own life and those of others is tremendous because ignorance or sloppiness in procedures can be fatal.

Weeks and weeks of study in the classrooms are combined with actual "hard hat" and SCUBA exercises in the "wet pot," or tank. Also at the school is a barge moored alongside from which training dives and underwater problems can be given. Students are dunked into the muddy Potomac to a depth of thirty feet, where they work with clumsy three-fingered gloves in total darkness.

One hurdle they must pass is the "Overhead Patch" problem. This consists of a patch two and one half feet in diameter attached to a platform underwater. The trick is to remove seventeen studs, being careful not to lose any of them, send the patch to the surface to satisfy instructors that the job has been done, then put it all back together again. The main difficulty is that the man must do this work *overhead*, and he must accomplish it in seventy minutes.

Another test involves two men working in a submerged pontoon. One man crawls inside the pontoon, which has a diameter of twenty-five inches, and attaches a patch (to show that he can work in a tight, enclosed area without getting claustrophobia) while the other man puts two patches on the outside. This job must be done in two hours, or the student does not pass.

But there comes a time when a diver really needs to know what it's like to go to sea with a diving gang, to handle the stage on which he will ride into the water, to buck the currents of a real body of water and otherwise to get the feel of this highly complicated equipment on which his life will depend.

A careful study of the Potomac River, which is extremely wide but unusually shallow, revealed a spot about sixty miles downriver from Washington, off Dahlgren, Virginia, where there is a hole about 100 feet deep and about 400 feet around. Here is where the student diving corpsman gets a taste of Fleet diving procedures while he is still in school.

Diving corpsmen play an important role at the school itself. One busy man is Chief Raymond Curran, who monitors the students' handling of the oxygen and helium fed to the divers. He also acts as "chambermaid" by going into the recompression chamber with anyone who might suffer an accident or an attack of the "bends." Chief Curran, who has been diving for thirteen years, has put in more than his share of time in the chamber, particularly at Pearl Harbor. Here, civilian skin divers who had no conception of the dangers of the depths periodically got into trouble. Curran would go into the chamber and give them full nursing care. On one occasion he spent sixty-nine hours in the chamber, caring for a man who was partially paralyzed. Curran lost eight pounds on that one.*

A recent graduate of the school is HM2 Bruce Field, a slight, five-foot-seven, 125-pound corpsman from Florida. He enlisted when he was seventeen, and after five and a half years with the Navy knows that he is a career corpsman. His reason for going through the deep-sea diving school is an unusual one because his final goal is to join the SEAL (Sea, Air, Land) Team of guerrilla warfare experts. He will be an underwater demolition expert, a precision parachutist, an accomplished linguist and a judo expert before he's done with it, but he knows he must be

* From an interview with the author.

familiar with everyone's job if he is to fulfill his primary purpose—taking care of the men.*

In the business of deep diving, the corpsman's responsibility for life and death is a part of his daily job. For instance, when a man surfaces without warning or explanation, the corpsman must evaluate the situation immediately. Is the man suffering from an air embolism, a massive bubble that can go to the heart,

* From an interview with the author.

First-class diving corpsman HM2 Bruce Field is suited up for an experimental dive at the Deep Sea Diving School in Washington, D.C. Field's goal is to join the Navy's SEAL (Sea, Air, Land) team. *U.S. Navy Photo*

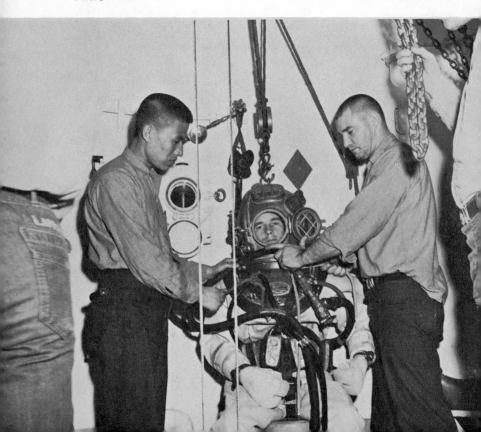

brain or chest cavity and be fatal within minutes? Does he have heat exhaustion, or is he drowning? If he is in pain, is it caused by the bends or a chain injury? Is it perhaps a combination of two or three problems?

The corpsman uses his medical knowledge by checking for signs of bleeding from the mouth or other symptoms. He calls upon his diving knowledge; he knows the type of dives and the equipment used. But he must commit himself immediately by treating the man for the worst of the symptoms. He may decide that mouth-to-mouth resuscitation and recompression are the only hope.

Sharing the same building with the Deep Sea Diving School is the Experimental Diving Unit. Three corpsmen work in this highly specialized unit, often volunteering as human subjects for testing equipment, diving techniques and working at extreme depths. In December 1964, two men went into the tank, or "wet pot," to make a 600-foot dive, the deepest for the entire Navy. One of the men is a corpsman, diving medical technician, HM1 Thomas W. James. Such deep dives will open the way for more effective submarine rescue work.

Duty for corpsmen aboard submarines has changed considerably in the past few years. For instance, in November 1960, there were eleven nuclear submarines in the Navy. As of July 1965, there are twenty-nine Fleet ballistic missile submarines of the Polaris type and twenty-two regular nuclear attack submarines, plus the twelve under construction. Twenty-nine attack submarines are under construction or are authorized. All Polaris submarines carry a submarine medical officer aboard, in addition to their corpsmen. Each also has "a blue and a gold" crew; that is, when one crew goes ashore for rest and recreation, the other crew takes over. The attack submarines still depend upon their independent-duty corpsmen for medical care.

Men aboard these boats live with a nuclear reactor for weeks at a time, but strangely enough they receive far less radiation than those who live ashore. This is because they are submerged for extended periods, and the water absorbs much of the cosmic radiation from the sun that they would receive ashore. They also are protected by the ship's hull.

The corpsmen's primary job is to see that life aboard the submarine is safe and comfortable. Every day they conduct tests at specified times, using portable and fixed instruments which are so sensitive they register radiation from harmless illuminated watches. For this reason, crew members are not allowed to wear watches with radium dials. A radiation check is made on the reactor's primary water system by sending tubes of water winding through the reactor. This water must remain at a specified level of radioactivity. Corpsmen "count" with electronic measuring devices in the ship's nucleonics laboratory.

Crew members can also check themselves for radiation. Each man must wear a pencil-like dosimeter and a film badge. Each man checks his dosimeter periodically by peering through it and reading the dosage scale. Film badges are collected and developed by the corpsmen for more detailed readings.

The amount of radiation per man is limited to five roentgens per year (a daily count is about 1/10,000th of a roentgen, or about what an average individual gets in two weeks on the surface). Another safety factor is a fresh flow of air. Nuclear submarines revitalize the same air many times. They also carry extra oxygen in tanks. Corpsmen make checks every few hours on this air supply. They see that it is fresh and cool by scrutinizing the oxygen, carbon dioxide, and hydrogen content of the ship's air.

To qualify for duty aboard nuclear submarines, corpsmen must spend six months to a year at the nuclear-power school after completion of their basic submarine and medical schooling.

This is topped off by three and a half months in the health physics course.

Ashore, corpsmen work in such highly specialized fields as the Radiation Exposure Evaluation Laboratory at the National Naval Medical Center, Bethesda, Maryland. Chief Petty Officer Donald Manley, radioisotope technician, describes the lab. It is divided into four rooms and is laid off in four chambers. Each door weighs four tons, but they are hinged so that they open fairly easily. In these chambers, the technicians "evaluate" about four patients a month, both civilian and military. This includes everyone who works in or near the Armed Forces Radiobiological Research Institute, or has been near a nuclear accident.

To measure radiation, Chief Manley puts the patient in a sort of couch, similar in design to what the Mercury astronauts were strapped into. Then he goes out of the chamber, closes the heavy door and turns on the 512-channel analyzer. In the counting chamber he watches the patient for ten minutes by closed-circuit television. After the information is "read out," the results are put on the oscilloscope. A permanent punch tape is made so that twenty years from now a comparison can be made. All employees of the AFRRI must have this count taken once a year—regardless.

Chief Manley hastens to explain that everyone is contaminated. "We all have cesium and potassium because of the fall-out of the bomb tests, but the amount is so small that it is harmless. We can even tell which patients normally drink a lot of milk. . . ." Radiation is excreted like any other poison, through the skin, kidneys or breath.

The lab is also involved in cancer detection and treatment. Their instruments scan the brain, kidney, thyroid, spleen, bone, heart or liver of the cancer victim.

Chief Manley is well qualified for the responsible position he holds today. In 1952, following his initial Hospital Corps school training, he went to the X-ray school at the Naval hospital in Philadelphia. From there he served on general duty in Guam, Saipan and Tinian in the Marianas Islands. He decided to try civilian life for three years, but because of his youthful appearance, the hospital where he worked would not give him a chance at the kind of responsibility he had been used to in the Navy.

In 1956, he went back into the service to work in a small radiation chamber. About this time, the Atomic Energy Commission sponsored a trip to Nevada to study the effects of radiation blast on man. In Manley's group were two third-class corpsmen, a civilian and two doctors. They took a truck and trailer, which was set up as a lab, complete with darkroom for developing film, and parked it all at News Nob.

Each time there was a nuclear test, Manley would go in five minutes later. The fireball was over his head, everything was dust and there was a grayish tinge everywhere. One time he mustered enough courage to look up. It scared him half to death, so he never did that again. Wearing a suit of coveralls, completely taped up with a mask, he carried two geiger counters. He knew that if the reading was off scale, he had better get out of there fast, or radio for help. He protected his instruments with aluminum foil. "You can see the noise. There is the ripple of cactus and stones and *bang* it's gone...."

Could a man who had been exposed to shock waves live in spite of heat and radiation? The results of these tests are secret, but obviously the closer to the bomb, the greater the casualties. Manley suggests that survival is possible 5,000 feet from ground zero and 40 degrees from radiation.

His adventuresome life continued at Pensacola, Florida, where he trained students and worked on the high-altitude balloon project of Dr. Ross and Dr. Prather. From that job he came to Bethesda for his present assignment. Manley is kept informed on the movement of all nuclear weapons, and is on call at all times, should an accident occur.*

As with other specialties, radioisotope technicians don't just happen. To begin with, corpsmen wanting to go into this field are carefully screened before admittance to the course. Even then, only about seventy-five percent of them make it through. There are tests all along the way, and even if it means studying until two or three in the morning, all tests must be passed.

The course is 960 hours long, with 385 hours in lectures and 575 hours in laboratory work. Subjects covered are orientation, radiation physics, mathematics, statistics, chemistry, radiation safety, clinical physiology, medical aspects of nuclear, biological and chemical warfare defense and leadership. There are twenty-one texts for study and reference. Among them are *Advanced Mathematics, College Chemistry, Physical Foundations of Radiology, Radiation Biophysics, Radiation Dosimetry, Radioactive Isotopes in Medicine and Biology,* and many others.

Recently, the Secretary of the Navy presented an Achievement Award to a corpsman who works in yet another highly specialized field. Hospital Corpsman First Class Marion E. Myers, a veteran of seventeen years of Naval service, has worked at the Air Crew Equipment Laboratory at the Naval Air Material Center, Philadelphia, Pennsylvania, since 1956. During this time, he has constantly volunteered for tests that exposed him to physical hazards above normal requirements for projects assigned to the Pressure Suit Research and Development Branch and the Mercury projects for NASA.

Myers, with his medical training, has been especially valuable as a test subject for obtaining data concerning physiological reaction and tolerance to certain emergency conditions that are likely to occur in the operation of high-altitude supersonic-speed

* From an interview with the author.

Naval aircraft. He voluntarily exposed himself to all phases of experimentation and testing associated with low-pressure chambers (at altitudes up to 100,000 feet), ejection seats and underwater survival studies.

Even though simulated or preliminary tests are conducted, Myers has subjected himself to conditions wherein equipment failure or human error could cause personal injury or death. For example, if a pressure-suit control system fails while at high altitude, loss of life could occur if the test chamber is not immediately brought to a livable altitude. If a failure such as a suit blowout is not predicted or anticipated, loss of life is highly probable.

The medic who works as a test subject for man's flight into space or into the ocean's depths has contributed tremendously to science and to the saving of lives. Even when he daily risks his own safety to do so, he loves his work and would have it no other way.

An "8492" or Special Operations Technician. This is the corpsman who serves with the Navy's Underwater Demolition Team (UDT) or with the SEALs, the Sea-Air-Land experts on guerrilla warfare. These corpsmen must be graduates of boot camp and a Class "A" corps school, must have on-the-job training experience at a "B" school, must be first-class divers, and must be graduates of the Fort Benning Jump School.

Training for UDT is the roughest the Navy can offer, and it is deliberately designed to discourage any man who is not physically fit or highly motivated enough for the job he will someday face. The attrition rate is about sixty-five percent.

Today, every platoon must have a diving corpsman. There must be five qualified corpsmen per team, so there are twenty-one or twenty-two at Little Creek, Virginia, and eleven or twelve at Coronado, California. In SEAL Teams One and Two, there are five corpsmen with each team. The most important spot in which a diving corpsman can serve the UDT and SEAL team is in the recompression chamber. Normally, it is the corpsman who decides on the length of time in the chamber and the pressure. A doctor is a rare luxury.

The Army at Fort Benning makes it rough for the Navy corpsman to get his parachute training. Instructors refer to the Navy's UDT men as "underwater ballerinas" and will often have them do their pushups in a sawdust pit that just happens to be half filled with water. But corpsmen must get through the rugged training, because when the SEALs go out of an airplane, it is the corpsman who jumps first in order to cover the rest of the jumpers.

The 8492s are cross-trained so that they can run the boat, the radio or other equipment. They are corpsmen for a while, then go on with other chores, and then become corpsmen again.

But with all the glamorous specialties of today's Navy corpsman, there is still the shipboard man who does just about the same jobs his predecessors did years ago. John Howery, HM3, who is presently a student at the pharmacy school at Portsmouth, enlisted in the Navy at seventeen, right out of high school. After boot camp and Hospital Corps school, he was sent to Guam for nineteen months, where he worked in the hospital on general duty and in the obstetrics ward. Later he boarded a cruiser and thought he was on his way back to the States where he could continue his schooling. Instead he was assigned to an oiler headed for the Far East: Korea, Japan, the Philippines and Hong Kong.

There was a senior chief petty officer to share his work and responsibilities, but no doctor. John was twenty years old and he realized that for the first time, he was really on his own. He would have to put into practice all the things he had been taught in school.

Because an oiler can be very dangerous, the sick bay was a

large one. Keeping it clean was difficult. John swears he practically crossed the Pacific on his hands and knees.

When he wasn't swabbing the sick-bay deck he was doing his routine tasks. Every morning at 0800 he held the first sick call. Although this was supposed to go on three times a day, men came in just about any time they needed to. He was literally on call all the time, but he liked it that way. He even slept in the sick bay. "For the first time in my life I had a room to myself...."

There was no such thing as a liberty status. If he did go any place, he left a telephone number where he could be reached. In Hong Kong, there didn't happen to be another ship in port where American medical attention could be given. There were no arrangements for the crew's care should they become ill or be injured, so he usually stuck close to them when they went ashore. The men knew he didn't have much help with his sick bay so if he ever needed anything done, all he had to do was ask and the fellows took care of him. The skipper always found time to listen to young Howery and invariably went along with his recommendations.

One of his jobs was preparing medications for his sick bay, but this was difficult to do. Because of the ship's vibrations and the rolling of the sea, he could not accurately weigh his ingredients. He had the same problem when the ship was in port, so one of his first jobs after docking was to go ashore to mix his medications. He bottled his elixir terpin hydrate and codeine cough syrup. He poured his benedryl into jugs and, for a sideline, filled bottles with milk of magnesia and other common remedies. Before the ship sailed, he had bottled up his aspirin tablets and vitamins and seen to it that the proper supply of antibiotics was aboard ship.

Young Howery remembers a case of appendicitis on that cruise. Both he and the other corpsman were in on the diagnosis, although John did the laboratory and clinical work. He did a complete blood count (CBC), a urinalysis, and took the patient's history (although he knew this pretty well after living aboard ship with the man). The jarring and rolling of the ship made the lab work difficult. It distorted the whole field, but the job got done.

The corpsmen reported their diagnosis to the skipper. There was no argument about the inconvenience a mistaken diagnosis might cause. If the corpsmen said the man required surgery and the care of a medical doctor, he would get it. Howery is proud of the fact that within six hours of their diagnosis, the patient was in surgery aboard an aircraft carrier.

John Howery got out of the Navy and went to college for a year. He worked nights in a civilian hospital but soon got bored because he was not allowed to do the kinds of things he had been used to doing in the Navy. He was never allowed to take tests to prove his knowledge and capabilities. "Sometimes I think they train you too well in the Navy. You see things that are being done wrong on the outside. It makes you mad, and nervous, too. . . ."

Another thing he noticed was that the Navy teaches corpsmen to operate and maintain medical equipment. A corpsman is expected to know how to take apart and put together all the machines and equipment he uses. "When I worked in the civilian hospital, I was the only man on night duty who knew how to use the respirator for asthmatic patients."

Howery wants to be a doctor. Considering his ability and background, the Navy will welcome him back to service as a full-fledged medical officer.*

In July 1949, the United States Air Force established its own Medical Service. Army personnel were given their choice of staying where they were or transferring to the Air Force. Many of the medical people had been deeply involved with the old Army Air Corps, so the switch to the new outfit was a natural

* From an interview with the author.

reaction. At that time 3,704 officers formed the nucleus of the Air Force Medical Service. Of these, 1,182 were medical officers, 424 dental, 78 veterinary corps, 733 medical service corps, 1,197 nurse corps and 90 women medical specialists corps. An acute problem arose when only 1,480 enlisted medics were allowed to transfer, although 8,837 were authorized and needed for the year 1950. By July 1950, there were 8,000 enlisted medics on duty at Air Force installations. Another 1,000 had been recalled to active duty, and by June 1952, with the Korean War, 27,316 Air Force medics were serving their country. Included in these figures are the many Navy hospital corpsmen who cast their lot with the Air Force. Today, any aeromedical technician with over sixteen years' service is naturally a veteran of the Army or Navy.

In many ways, the training of the Air Force medic resembles that of the other services because, of course, he serves in hospitals, clinics and dispensaries at Air Force installations around the world. But there are specialties peculiar to the Air Force, just as there are specialties within the Army and the Navy. It all depends on the mission.

The Air Force medic receives his preliminary training at Lackland Air Force Base, San Antonio, Texas. Every week, some seventy-five "basics" are selected to enter the Medical Helper Course conducted by the Air Training Command. Here, while military basic is going on, students get 120 hours of classroom instruction in the fundamentals of military medicine, including the organization and mission of the USAF Medical Service.

Classes assemble at 0700 for studies in anatomy and physiology. Following their exams, students are introduced to a mockup of a hospital ward where they learn about the dozens of chores necessary to running a hospital. Students take turns acting the part of patients as they attack problems ranging from the pedestrian but important art of making a bed properly to the procedures for isolating contagious-disease cases. There is also realistic field training where fledgling medics learn to care for battle casualties, including control of hemorrhage, treatment of shock and medical evacuation techniques.

There are tests, examinations and observations throughout this preliminary and elementary course. Facts are fed into a computer, which in turn indicates what the next step will be. Some men are immediately sent to medical facilities within the United States or overseas where they continue their on-the-job training. The largest percentage moves to the Medical Service School at Gunter Air Force Base in Alabama for more specialized training. Some graduates go to Brooks Air Force Base in Texas for special courses in the Aerospace Medical Division.

As with the other services, the Air Force receives a cross section of the nation's population. It is up to the military to bring out the best in each man. Major General Kenneth E. Pletcher, Deputy Surgeon General, USAF, remembers the problem at Carswell Air Force Base in Texas. "We had 103 enlisted men, all of whom had been classified as 'untrainable,' and they were all assigned to the Air Force Medical Service."

General Pletcher immediately asked his first sergeant to arrange for a conference with his new "medics." Then he told them of his sentiments. "I don't believe that you American boys are untrainable and I don't believe you think so either. Now, I want each of you to go to your first sergeant and tell him what you think you want to do. I want to know what kind of on-the-job training you would really like. The only thing I am asking of you is that you produce."

Although General Pletcher had no idea whether or not the idea would work, he noted that the boys did see their first sergeants for their assignments. Some wanted to work in the surgical ward; others wanted to help keep the hospital clean; others were interested in pediatrics or in laboratory work. Some boys wanted to change jobs after they'd given the first choice a try. They were allowed to do this. "I insisted that they all wear name tags so that I could call them each by name."

"Within a year we had trained all but six of these 'untrainables.' Some went on with their careers and made tech sergeant. Ten years later they were still serving in the Air Force."

General Pletcher explains the reason for this success story. "The problem with psychological testing is that most often it leaves out motivation, the kind that comes from a family group, USAF, feeling. Those men were confused, they thought nobody cared about them. But when we showed an interest in their progress by going to see them on the job, remembering their names and encouraging them, they got along just fine."*

Another training program that General Pletcher fathered is the advanced course for independent-duty aeromedical technicians given at the USAF School of Aerospace Medicine, Brooks Air Force Base, in Texas. As with the Navy corpsmen serving with the Marines and aboard ship, the Air Force medic must prepare himself to serve in any one of hundreds of isolated outposts where officers and airmen are on duty. And because there are not enough doctors to go around, he must carry this responsibility alone.

To qualify for this seventeen-week course, the man must be a grade seven or above. He must be in excellent physical condition and have a mental rating of "superior."

The medical courses include physiology, pharmacology, eye, ear, nose, and throat conditions, internal medicine, surgery and dentistry. There is also training in preventive medicine, aeromedical evacuation and problems of high-altitude flight. A special class teaches conditions prevailing in the Arctic, emphasizing injuries and diseases of that area.

For an independent-duty med tech, the accuracy of his diagnosis is all-important. It is he who decides whether he can treat

* From an interview with the author.

Patients from all over Europe are brought to Rhein Main Air Base in Germany for aeromedical evacuation to hospital centers in the United States. Flight nurses and med techs care for patients during the overwater flight. *U.S. Air Force Photo*

the patient himself, or whether the patient should be evacuated to the nearest medical installation. If the patient cannot be moved, he can radio for a doctor.

His routine responsibilities are the usual daily sick call, treatment of minor ailments, inspections of mess halls and sanitary facilities and monthly physical examinations. He is trained to set fractures in traction and to clean wounds. In an emergency he could do a tracheotomy and treat emotional disorders until the patient could be removed to a hospital.

An important specialty of Air Force med techs is that of aeromedical evacuation. The concept of using airplanes as flying ambulances or hospitals is not a new one; through the years air pioneers have experimented with all sorts of planes and equipment. It was not until World War II that the first large-scale combat aeromedical evacuation was used. Medics assigned to the United States Army Air Forces gave in-flight care to some 1,300,000 casualties being moved to medical facilities away from the fighting fronts. Aircraft used during this period were largely bomber types such as the B-17, the B-24, the B-25 and B-26. There were also the C-47, C-46 and single-engine L-5B liaison aircraft, which could carry a litter.

Air evacuation was not planned or organized at the start of the war, and the medics had no special training in on-loading and off-loading of patients. They were not schooled in the special problems of medical treatment at altitude in unpressurized cabins. These men often found themselves hitchhiking to the front-line holding positions, picking up their patients and then trying to hitch a ride back for their patients and themselves. To secure patients in flight, medics tied them to the floor with ropes.

As the war progressed, improvements in the system were made; techniques and equipment were developed and medics and nurses were trained to care properly for patients in flight.

Following the end of hostilities, air evacuation for military patients requiring transport was continued. In September 1949, the Secretary of Defense directed that evacuation of all sick and wounded, in peace and war, should be accomplished by air. Only in unusual circumstances would hospital ships and other surface transport be used.

Air evacuation of patients during the Korean conflict was largely performed by helicopters. The wounded were lifted from near the front lines to airstrips where troop-carrier planes airlifted them to hospitals in Japan, and the Military Air Transport Service (MATS) transported them across the Pacific. Doctors, nurses and medical technicians waited for the wounded at airstrips in Korea and cared for the patients aboard the transports. These teams attended 296,328 patients in Korea and Japan and more than 63,000 patients on transpacific flights. During the Korean conflict, ninety-five percent of all medical evacuations were made by air. Unlike the medics of World War II, med techs in Korea had been trained for eleven weeks in the special problems they would face. They had new equipment, such as the Stryker frame for transporting patients with spinal injuries and burns, and their planes had stanchions which held litters in tiers.

Aeromedical techniques continued to advance during the 1950's with patients being moved in the C-118 Liftmaster, C-119 twin-tailed transports, C-124 Globemasters and C-131 specially equipped hospital aircraft. Many of these aircraft continue to service European and Asiatic installations while jet aircraft perform the Pacific and Atlantic hops. In October 1961, the giant C-135 Stratolifter went into service to transport patients twice weekly from Rhein Main Air Base, near Frankfurt, Germany to McGuire Air Force Base, New Jersey. Carrying 33 litter and 44 seated patients, the nonstop flight lasts a little over eight hours.

A relatively small group of medical airmen in the Air Force devote full time to the unique occupation of indoctrinating flying personnel in the physiological stresses encountered in flight. These men are designated as physiological training technicians.

The development of this specialty is the result of the work of dedicated scientists during the World War II era who realized that air crew members would be flying well above 30,000 feet. Between 1942 and 1946, over a million men drilled in the exposures that pilots, bombardiers and navigators would experience in low-pressure chambers with the lowered barometric pressures found at high altitudes. These men learned about the effects of altitude on their bodies, the need for oxygen, how to use oxygen and other protective equipment. They were also taught the principles of emergency survival, night vision and how to protect against and cope with "G" forces.

In 1949, the program was reactivated to cope with the new jets coming off the assembly lines, with pressurized cabins and ejection seats. The program was also designed to indoctrinate pilots and crews on the use of the partial pressure suits for flights above 50,000 feet.

Med techs have been deeply involved with these training programs for about ten years. The six-week course for supervisors was established in 1956 at the Gunter Branch of the Air Force School of Aviation Medicine in Alabama. Today, these med techs work in "PTUs," physiological training units, in the United States and overseas. Each unit is equipped with a low-pressure chamber, a night-vision trainer and an ejection-seat training device. The standard low-pressure chamber simulates altitudes up to 43,000 feet. It is divided into a main compartment seating eighteen men and a "lock" used as an emergency means of exit when an evacuation at altitude must take place. The "lock" is also used for rapid decompression, or the simulating of a sudden loss of pressure. Units are fitted with all the current types of oxygen regulators and the latest aircraft communication equipment.

Medics who work in the PTU business have tremendous responsibilities. Their decisions can literally mean life or death to the air crews they are training. These men must not only know how to operate and maintain the low-pressure chamber, the vacuum pumps, oxygen and communications equipment, but, depending on whether he is an "inside" observer or an "outside" one, he must be constantly on the alert for danger signs. He must be able to recognize early symptoms of such altitude reactions as hypoxia, hyperventilation, neurocirculatory collapse and decompression sickness (bends). And he must know how to handle them immediately. The "inside" instructor, riding shotgun, must be ready to take immediate corrective action when a student experiences any of the altitude reactions.

Duty as an "inside" instructor is hazardous; each "flight" is an exposure to an environment in which the instructor can get the bends. Most PTU medics suffer periodically from ear problems or postnasal drip, or both.

Air Force medic, TSgt. William Henderson (right), explains the finer points of space-age cooking to Captain William D. Habluetzel inside the two-man space cabin simulator at the School of Aerospace Medicine, Brooks Air Force Base, Texas. The "flight" was designed to test the reliability of component parts of the simulator and to obtain data relevant to planned Gemini flights. *USAF Photo*

A parasite chamber is used in connection with the main chamber for partial pressure-suit training. Malfunction of the equipment at, say, 65,000 feet could cause the trainee to become unconscious in a very few seconds. Here again is a serious responsibility for the training technician.

Air Force medics have long been instrumental in aerospace test projects. As early as 1947, Colonel John Paul Stapp worked with and trained enlisted specialists on the famed sled rides for the study of the effects of acceleration and deceleration on the human body. Colonel Stapp remembers the devotion to duty of his medic assistants at Holloman Air Force Base. "Med techs volunteered for all kinds of tests. A doctor would draw their blood before they 'rode the sled,' and afterward they would do their own lab work. They would simply stagger off the sled and go to work. . . ." At Holloman, Senior Master Sergeant Marvin A. Bernhard taught himself to be an X-ray technician. Colonel Stapp had some fifty-eight volunteers for his important projects, but he always knew who was obeying the rules and doing the test work right. "The medics always came through. . . .*

Technical Sergeant Hobart Craft had been in the service for seventeen years by the time he made his record "flight" in a spacecraft simulator in 1960. Fourteen of these years had been spent as a Navy corpsman with duty in the South Pacific during World War II and later in Korea. He joined the Air Force in 1956 and, after a tour of duty in Florida, came to the School of Aerospace Medicine at Brooks Air Force Base, Texas. Prior to the Gemini flights he and Technical Sergeant William Henderson spent fourteen days in the two-man simulator in order to monitor the cabin machinery.

The cabin itself is elliptical in shape, eight feet high and twelve feet long, and is capable of maintaining two people for up to thirty days. There is a single door and a small airlock through which necessary items can be passed without affecting the cabin pressure, and without direct contact between the occupants and scientists outside. Although the two men had some of the comforts of home, such as easy chairs, a bed, sanitary facilities, food and a device for warming it, they were constantly on television as they went about their duties of answering questions, taking blood samples from each other, operating the water recycling unit—as well as constantly checking their myriad control systems.

The list of test subjects among the medics of all three services is endless, and their contributions to science continues to be of vital importance. SMSgt. James Ferguson, biodynamics technician at the Aeromedical Research Laboratory, Holloman Air Force Base, has ridden the Daisy Decelerator some 250 times. SSgt. Edwin Osbon, NCOIC of the centrifuge unit at the USAF School of Aerospace Medicine, has ridden the centrifuge to the seven-G level. MSgt. Robert J. Koch, physiology training supervisor, and A1C John Lingafeter, physiological

* From an interview with the author.

training specialist, USAF School of Aerospace Medicine, were medics who were two of four subjects in a series of "bends" tests to determine protective measures for future space pilots. TSgt. Thomas C. White, anatomy instructor at the same school, was named outstanding airman for the Aerospace Medical Division for 1964. SSgt. John Rivenburgh, medical technician at the Air Force Hospital, Lackland Air Force Base, Texas, devised and improvised a lymphatic infuser and a kidney-carrier receptacle, both of which are in use with the hospital's kidney transplant program and are expected to be maunfactured commercially. Another outstanding airman, a veteran surgical technician of the World War II campaigns of Leyte and Mindora, MSgt. Robert L. McLaughlin of the Air National Guard, designed a device which automatically inflates air-crew flotation gear.

An unusual group of Air Force men who are medically trained, but who do not come under the command of the Air Force Medical Service, are the Pararescuemen of Air Rescue Service. This elite group are experts at parachuting into remote areas to rescue downed flyers or, for that matter, anyone who requires medical attention immediately. They parachute onto ice caps and cliffs, into the water and steaming jungles, and behind enemy lines in order to save lives. At present there are 155 of these men working with Air Rescue squadrons scattered around the world.*

Although medics are military men and have become highly specialized in their respective fields, they have always played an important role in helping civilians in time of trouble. There is probably no natural disaster involving human lives in which medics are not dispatched to render first aid, give inoculations, purify water and distribute food, evacuate casualties and take on just about any job that needs doing. As early as 1908, Navy

* Eloise Engle, *Pararescue* (New York: The John Day Company, 1964).

Medically trained pararescuemen of the USAF parachute to the aid of survivors of aircraft accidents or anyone else who cannot otherwise be given immediate medical aid. *USAF Photo*

After the fall of Dien Bien Phu, Navy corpsmen took care of Vietnamese refugees on the trip to South Vietnam. *U.S. Navy Photo*

corpsmen attached to the fleet at Alexandria were immediately sent to Messina to render first aid following the Mount Etna eruption. In 1923 they were rushed to Yokohama, following the disastrous earthquake and fire. Corpsmen were in Greece following the 1954 earthquake, and when a hurricane struck Haiti that year, the U.S.S. *Saipan* sailed in with her corpsmen to help the stricken people. The 1955 hurricane struck Tampico, Mexico, and again the U.S.S. *Saipan* was there with beans, C-rations, water and corpsmen. A major job for Navy corpsmen was the 1954 evacuation of 200,000 refugees to Saigon after the fall of Dien Bien Phu in Indochina. Medical problems were enormous; skin, eye and scalp infections, dysentery, malaria and the entire spectrum of tropical diseases had to be coped with as the ships, loaded to the gunwales, set out on the four-day voyage. Corpsmen used twelve tons of DDT during the eight-month period it took to move the Vietnamese people to Saigon. They took care of babies and old people, they comforted the frightened and the sad on that strange journey that fate and world politics had forced them into.

Army medics in Europe routinely go into disaster areas to give what help they can. In 1962 when Iran was badly hit by an earthquake, the Army sent a hospital to the area and flew their aidmen in helicopters to isolated spots in the mountains. In Morocco, displaced people who had had to leave their homes during the flood of 1963 were seriously endangered by the threat of epidemics. The Moroccan government asked for help, and they got it. Eight officers and eight enlisted medics, broken up into five teams, arrived with their DDT powder and spray for the tents and homes, typhoid serum and chlorine and lime for purifying well water. For the first time the Moroccans saw the jet gun used for mass immunization. Eventually, 60,000 people were protected from typhoid fever following jet-gun immunization.

Medics work well as a team, but basically they are trained to make independent decisions, particularly in an emergency. Seaman Second Class Frank Hinton was riding the New York subway during the morning rush hour when he noticed a commotion in the front of the car. Something was going on, and he suspected that it might have to do with the pregnant woman he had seen entering the car. When the train stopped, Hinton managed to elbow his way onto the platform and dart back into the front of the car just as the doors were closing. He still could not see the woman, but he shouldered his way through the crowd, produced his Navy identification card, and told everyone to get out of the way. Birth had already started when he reached her. Hinton immediately sent the woman's sister to tell the conductor to stop the subway, but it was five stations later before word could be got to him. Meanwhile, the young Navy corpsman proceeded to deliver the eight-pound baby and clip the umbilical cord with scissors from a bystander's handbag. He sterilized the scissors over a fire made of trash. He wrapped the baby in newspapers and handed it to its mother. At Greenpoint Hospital, the medical superintendent pronounced, "Mother and child are fine."

Chief Hospital Corpsman Robert Lee Williams, on duty at the United States Navy and Marine Corps Reserve Training Center in Jackson, Michigan, was on the scene at 1:30 P.M. when an office building under construction suddenly collapsed. Williams immediately went to work rendering first aid and helping out wherever he could. He voluntarily remained on duty until 6:30 the next morning, when he was relieved by the civilian first-aid team.

Hospital Corpsman First Class Nicholas R. Couture, serving aboard the U.S.S. *Davis*, was enjoying a relatively uneventful trip from Bermuda to Newport, Rhode Island, when word was received that a crewman aboard the Swedish flag tanker *Seven Skies* had a severe scalp wound and was bleeding profusely. Could a corpsman be put aboard the tanker to give first aid? In spite of the heavy swells on the high seas, the transfer was made.

Couture managed to stop the bleeding from the wound and then sutured the torn scalp back in place.

Corpsmen, of course, are only human, and in their enthusiasm for being of service they can sometimes get carried away. The *Hospital Corps Quarterly* cites an example. It seems that "Skinhead" Harper and "Feet" Nelson, both HA deuces at the San Diego Hospital Corps School, were parading up and down Broadway near the Plaza one Saturday afternoon, their shining Red Cross badges visible for all who passed them on the port side.

Unexpectedly, some fifty or so feet ahead of them, a two-wheeled "death chariot" motorcycle leaped the curb and side-swiped a pedestrian on the sidewalk. The inevitable crowd materialized, and by the time the two heroic, embryonic "doctor's mates" arrived, they had to shoulder their way through the mob.

On reaching the center, they took charge and began to clear the area around the prostrate pedestrian by forcibly pushing those nearest to the rear, directing at the same time that "someone call an ambulance," "someone else tear up a petticoat for bandages," and a third person "help maintain quiet."

Just as the crowd was beginning to purr its admiration of the hospital corpsmen for the orderly manner in which the situation was being handled, "Skinhead" looked over the crowd and inquired, "Has anyone got a thermometer?"

It is impossible even to estimate the number of lives saved by medics who work in the field of epidemiology and preventive medicine. Medics in all three services work in units spread around the world, from the tropics to the Arctic and the Antarctic. Among the busiest of these units is the Naval Medical Research Unit Number Three (NAMRU 3) located in Cairo, Egypt. Corpsmen here work with Egyptian doctors and a small number of American Naval and civilian personnel. The 1,500-

bed hospital cares for patients over a long period of time, with controlled observations on diagnostic procedures, therapy and so on. The stress here is in the field of biology dealing with arthropods (insects and spiders), and the knowledge gained is of benefit to all the free world.

NAMRU 2 is located at the northern extreme of Taiwan. The primary purpose of this unit is to obtain basic information on tropical and subtropical diseases. The twelve corpsmen working at NAMRU 2 as laboratory and chemistry technicians have been instrumental in developing new diagnostic techniques for parasitic infections, a promising new vaccine for trachoma, new methods of treating cholera victims and improved control of Japanese B encephalitis. There are millions and millions of people in this area of the world who, because of substandard diet, poor sanitary conditions, and lack of medical care, are at least mildly sick. Workers at NAMRU 2 are seeking a way of eliminating diseases or at least treating them effectively.

Most of the professional, technical and administrative staff members of the unit are Chinese nationals who are under contract to the Taiwan University Hospital. And because corpsmen are working directly with local doctors and health officials, they must be unusually good, mature and senior men. The lowest-rating corpsman at NAMRU 2 is an HM2.

The unit has been under the command of Captain Robert A. Phillips, MC, USN for the past nine years, and in that time he has become well known all over the area. For instance, should an epidemic break out, the embassy of the country affected will issue a formal request for help. Corpsmen go with teams to Thailand, South Vietnam, North Borneo, Australia, Indonesia, the Philippines, Okinawa, Korea and the Pescadores. They collect blood and stool samples and, if it is a parasitology study, they collect parasites from animals and migratory birds. They study snakes and snails as disease spreaders and the encephalitis virus recovered from thousands of mosquitoes, most of them from

Taiwan or Okinawa. Up to 100,000 mosquitoes trapped in these countries were separated by species and tested for infection during a recent study.

Corpsmen's lives at NAMRU vary from working in the quiet solitude of the laboratory to bouncing over primitive countryside in jeeps or station wagons. They double as collectors of data and observers of their work. And always they must be tactful in their dealings with the medical workers who are their hosts. An example of such tact can be found in Chief Hospitalman John Ramps, whose job it was to train foreign doctors in the new techniques for treating cholera victims. He got along so well with this assignment that doctors would actually request instruction from him. The new treatment for cholera was developed by Captain Phillips, who had used it during World War II for burn cases. It consists of replacing body fluids through intravenous feedings. The trick lies in first determining the state of dehydration and then, by working out a formula, maintaining the fluid at a mathematically determined level. Before this system was adopted, sixty percent of all cholera victims who were not treated, died, and twenty-four percent of those under treatment died. Now, all cholera victims under the new treatment are almost certain to recover.

Through the years, medics have trained and gone to school in order to become specialists in their chosen fields. They have aided civilian populations in time of disaster and worked to prevent and cure disease. But in the meantime, combat medics found themselves once more on the field of battle. This time it was in Korea.

9

Working Together in Korea

"I lied about my age of sixteen when I enlisted in the Army. At eighteen I was an aidman in Korea, looking after forty guys. It was like having a family of forty kids. You cry with them, take care of them when they're sick and injured. . . . It was a staggering responsibility. Everybody said, 'Do me a miracle. I'm dying. Make me stand up and walk.' Many times you can't do that. . . ."

—Sergeant Fred Brockbank, E-7*

O N June 25, 1950, the armies of North Korea, a protégé of the Soviet Union and of Communist China, invaded South Korea across the 38th parallel. The United Nations Security Council branded North Korea an aggressor, and on June 27, President Harry Truman ordered United States air and sea forces to assist the South Koreans in defending themselves.

Fourteen United Nations members joined the United States in the fight to stop Communist aggression. The "police action" turned into a bloody, hideous retreat for the United Nations

* From an interview with the author.

forces as the Communists pushed them down and nearly into the sea at Pusan.

The United Nations forces held at the Pusan beachhead through battle after battle until the Reds were turned back. With the Eighth Army continuing the fight in South Korea, United Nations forces totaling 40,000, under the command of General Douglas MacArthur, made a waterborne invasion at Inchon. Seoul, South Korea's capital city, was liberated. The United Nations forces pushed northward, close to Manchuria, only to be forced back by the surprise attacks of hordes of Communist Chinese. The newspapers began calling the police action a "yo-yo war," among other things. The medical departments had long since recognized the Korean conflict as the most awesome task they had yet faced.

To begin with, they were badly unprepared for the sudden outbreak of hostilities. Their hospitals, hospital ships and training facilities had been deactivated, or put into mothballs, following World War II. The supply of medical officers, aidmen and corpsmen with previous combat experience or recent field training was extremely limited. Medical supplies were geared to peacetime activities. There were few medical facilities in the area and none in Korea, with the exception of the Army's MAAG dispensary at Seoul. There were several fixed Army hospitals in Japan and one Navy dispensary in Yokosuka. The hospital ship U.S.S. *Consolation* was operating off the east coast of the United States, thousands of miles away from the combat zone. The Air Force medical department, less than a year old, was operating with a fraction of its needed and authorized personnel. Medical intelligence was almost entirely dependent upon what the Japanese had learned about the area.

To make matters worse, the small medical forces were faced with caring for patients under the most unfavorable environmental conditions in history. Dysentery, diarrhea, enteritis, malaria, venereal disease and epidemic louse-borne typhus fever were a few of the diseases that had long caused severe morbidity among the natives. Before United Nations medical-control measures took over in 1951, there were 7,515 cases of typhoid reported among the civilians and 3,915 cases of small-pox. Leprosy and tuberculosis were common diseases.

After the sweltering heat of the summer, fighting was centered on the tops of frozen mountain ridges and in snow-filled valleys near the Manchurian border, where the variation in temperature was often seventy-five degrees between daybreak and nightfall. There were the unstabilized battle lines to cope with and the movement of refugees, all of whom harbored infection and disease. Another problem was the care and treatment of the prisoners of war. After the Chinese intervened in November, 1950, and the ensuing United Nations offensive into North Korea, many troops lost much of their clothing and equipment. There were 3,000 cases of frostbite in the Marine Corps and Navy during this period, and many more in the Army. Because of the desperate fighting conditions, medical workers could not practice the preventive medicine they had struggled so long to develop. With the repeated isolation and encirclement of holding troops through the rice paddies and rugged hills, United Nations troops suffered badly from epidemic hemorrhagic fever and Japanese B encephalitis. Korea's severe cold was bad for Americans who had never been exposed to such climates, but it was disastrous to the troops who had lived their entire lives in the tropics: the Filipinos, the Thai and the Ethiopians.

And in the midst of all the heavy fighting, the disease, the filth and the cold, came the heavy rains in the spring which turned the bumpy little north-south roads into soggy morasses. It was over these "roads" that the medics traveled with their heavy trucks carrying tents, poles, medical supplies and portable equipment.

Yet, in spite of the obstacles and the seemingly hopeless situation in Korea, the medical departments of the Army, Navy and

Air Force performed in the most brilliant manner in wartime history. Hundreds of thousands of lives were saved that a few years before would have been lost. Doctors, nurses and medical technicians, aidmen and corpsmen all worked together, regardless of creed, color or branch of service. There were points in their favor—new drugs, improved field surgical techniques and the massive use of plasma to save lives—but most important, there was the incredible efficiency of the system known as air evac (aeromedical evacuation) which carried the wounded to aid stations and hospitals within minutes after being injured.

Since there were no Army field hospitals in Korea at the beginning of hostilities, several units were quickly organized in Japan. Later, others were organized in the States and sent to the war zone. In June 1950, the 8055 MASH (Mobile Army Surgical Hospital) landed in Pusan with the infantry units. Following this hospital were the 8063, the 8076 and a fourth, manned by personnel from Norway and commanded by a Norwegian surgeon. The staff of each hospital included two anesthesiologists, a bone surgeon, an internist and a dental surgeon. With the chief nurse were two nurse anesthetists, four surgical and ten general-duty nurses. Three housekeeping officers took care of supplies, records and tented trucks. The 121 enlisted men were augmented by Koreans. Their job was to carry litters down the assembly line, load and unload trucks and drive them on "bug-outs," erect tents, keep pegs tightened, tend generators and stoves, string wires and lay fuel and water pipe. They were to make carpentry repairs and dig foxholes for defense against attacks. In general, the Army tried to set up MASH hospitals in a manner similar to civilian ones, with a receiving tent, emergency treatment rooms, an X-ray room and an operating room. Some of these mobile units, designed to carry 60 casualties, wound up taking care of 300 to 400 men. They were constantly on the move, back and forth, wherever the front-line fighting was going on. One unit moved nineteen times in seven months.

One month after the war's beginning, the hospital ship U.S.S. *Consolation* arrived at the Pusan pier to receive casualties. The Yokosuka dispensary had been expanded, and additional medical personnel had been assigned to Military Air Transport Service (MATS) and Military Sea Transport Service (MSTS) for the removal of casualties. The hospital ships U.S.S. *Repose* and U.S.S. *Haven* were dispatched to Korea. These ships, where definitive care under sterile hospital conditions could be given, were a tremendous help to the overworked forces ashore. During the first three days after the *Consolation*'s arrival at Pusan, her litter hoists were in constant use. At the Pusan railroad station 1,327 wounded were met by ambulances and rushed to the dockside.

The Marines' first projected campaign in Korea was to require 18 medical officers and 184 hospital corpsmen, but by September 1950, with the First Marine Division operating at wartime strength, this number had to be increased to 71 medical officers and 997 corpsmen. A Field Medical Service School was hastily established in October 1950 at Camp Lejeune, North Carolina, for training officers and enlisted men in the basic principles of field medicine. In the following nine months, over 250 medical officers, 75 dental officers and 2,000 corpsmen were graduated from this school and assigned to combat field units. Also, the Field Medical Service Battalion was activated at Camp Pendleton, California, for full training and physical conditioning of hospital corpsmen. Over 1,200 hospital corpsmen received their basic field training at this facility in the first few months of the war. The First Force Evacuation Hospital was activated in October 1950, with 21 medical officers, 2 dental officers and 246 corpsmen. It was the first of its kind ever commissioned within the Fleet Marine Force. A pool of Navy medical and dental service personnel, specially trained for combat duty, was created. Rotating every ten months would be 125 medical officers, 15 medical service corps officers and 1,400 corpsmen. These trained men were assigned to replacement pools and committed to medical and dental support of the First Marine Division, Fleet Marine Force, the Pacific. At the peak of the Marine Corps operations in Korea, 25 surgical teams, consisting of a surgeon, an assistant surgeon, an anesthetist and ten specially trained hospital corps-men, were flown to areas as needed or were used aboard casualty carrying ships or hospitals at home and abroad.

Meanwhile, as the medical departments hurriedly trained men and expanded their facilities, the fierce battles raged on. And it was not the kind of fighting remembered by veterans of the World War II campaigns in Europe, who could go for days without seeing a live enemy soldier. In Korea, it was Indian-style, hand-to-hand, bloody combat.

Medics worked all the time, everywhere. Sometimes they crawled over the field of battle carrying canteens of water and syrettes of morphine to those who needed relief. Litter bearers were again at their age-old duties. And the wounded watched, waited, numb with shock or exhaustion, shivering with pain or heat, sick with thirst or hunger.

Scenes at the MASH hospitals were ever-changing, never the same, yet there were also terrible rituals to be performed. When the vehicle brought a wounded man in from the front-line aid station, the medics closed in on him as a team; one grabbed an arm and began transfusing a pint of blood while another injected a shot of morphine in the other arm. If the wounded was in such bad shape that his breathing had stopped, the med-ics quickly gave him artificial respiration by grabbing his arms and moving them up and down. As this was happening, the blood team got a needle into the fast-moving arm. Meanwhile another team cut off the man's clothes. The clothes, filled with blood and holes from mortar and grenade fragments, some-times became twisted in with the mangled flesh and had to be removed by surgery, under ether.

Medics working in MASH surgery acted as "circulators." They tied the doctors' gowns, sterilized instruments, opened sterile linen and counted the sponges in use. If respiration stopped during surgery, the nurses and doctors backed off while two corpsmen gave artificial respiration. It was often the medic who stood by the patient when he came out from under the ether following an amputation. And it was he who told the man that the limb was gone.

Medics stood by when the patient came out of the ether because sometimes he was delirious. The medic had to hold the

A grief-stricken American infantryman whose buddy has been killed in action is comforted by another soldier. In the background, a corpsman fills out casualty tags. Korea, August 28, 1950. *U.S. Army Photo*

man down to keep him from smashing the apparatus of blood or plasma needles, casts, traction pulleys or tubes that were inserted in his nose for draining stomach juices during surgery.

There were those who never made it to the MASH hospital or to the airplane that would carry them home. Sergeant Fred Brockbank, one of four aidmen with "I" Company of the 23rd Infantry Rifle Company, remembers the battle near Taegu. Eighteen men were killed in fifteen minutes, including the commanding officer, Captain Jackson. Brockbank saw that his buddy, a medic named Roberts, was hit. Both legs were blown off. "I started crawling up the hill to get him. I finally made it and put tourniquets on what was left of his legs. Damn fool just looked at me and said, 'Don't worry about it,' and then he died. . . ."*

The medics as well as the troops had rules to go by. They were not supposed to run pell mell into the thick of things every time they heard the call "Medic!" particularly when the enemy so often used this call as a ruse to flush these valued aidmen into open target range. And troops had been instructed to call out the medic's personal name rather than just "Help" or "Medic!" Sometimes it happened to work out that way, sometimes it didn't. The medics went out, no matter what kind of distress call they heard.

Medics were supposed to make out an emergency medical tag and attach it to each casualty they treated. But in heavy combat, "Anybody who can take fifteen minutes out to do this kind of paper work isn't busy. . . ." If morphine had been administered, medics sometimes hastily scrawled "M," in blood, on the wounded man's forehead. "Or you can use dirt or mud. . . ." Twigs tied to the tourniquet also indicated that morphine had been administered. "If a man is unconscious you give him a quarter of a grain of morphine. If he's a big guy he can

* From an interview with the author.

take a half grain. Sometimes when you run short, you have to use one syrette for two people. That's not good, but it's better than nothing."

Medics are not supposed to perform surgery. Sergeant Brockbank remembers September 16, 1950. "We were moving across the Naktong River to the Yalu. This one particular battle lasted only a few short minutes but two out of three platoon leaders were killed. Of the two platoon sergeants, one was killed. I had been wounded that morning, but I was still going. There was so much to do. Enemy tanks were attacking and about that time the Korean Self Defense Force propelled their gunfire. They were firing over us to get at the enemy tanks when suddenly they dropped their fire fifty feet and that's when we got it—

Members of the 231st Transportation Truck Battalion, 2nd Log. Comd., deliver a patient to a helicopter at the I Corps Area, Chonan, Korea, to be evacuated to a hospital behind the front lines. February 11, 1951. *U.S. Army Photo*

bad. First Lieutenant Dorsey Labert, such a fine fellow and a good leader, his leg was all but blown off. He was bleeding badly. I went up the hill to get him. I gave him morphine, applied a tourniquet and then . . . I had to do it. He was my friend, too. I really admired him. I amputated his leg with my bayonet, carried him down the hill and gave him to the litter bearers."*

That night, Brockbank was put aboard a hospital train for treatment of his own wounds. The lieutenant was aboard the same train, and the two men talked together. The eighteen-year-old medic said he was sorry he had to take the officer's leg that way. Labert shook his head and said he knew it was necessary. And then he thanked Brockbank for saving his life.

Doctors later amputated the lieutenant's leg at a higher point because of the shattered bone.

In the meantime, Navy corpsmen were traveling with the Marines.

On October 7, 1950, the First Marine Division was relieved by the Eighth Army and on the 29th of that month sailed around the peninsula and landed at Wonsan, near Hungnam. The Seventh Marines at that time did have a large-scale fight with Chinese Communists who had infiltrated through the mountains to aid the beaten North Koreans. Nevertheless, the Marines were ordered to advance up the road seventy-eight miles from Hungnam to Yudam-ni, a tiny village west of the Chosin Reservoir.

These Marines and their corpsmen were battle-hardened veterans of the amphibious landings and running battles that reconquered Seoul and broke the North Koreans' back. Practically all their noncommissioned officers were veterans of World War II Pacific campaigns. It is no exaggeration to say that the

* From an interview with the author.

First Marine Division was the most seasoned striking force in United States history.

North Korea, November 1950. The Marines and their corpsmen moved through the freezing blizzards in temperatures of twenty-five degrees below zero. The narrow roads became sheets of rutted ice; weapons and equipment glistened and hardened with frost. Men pinned down by the enemy in their snow bunkers found their feet encased in blocks of ice. Soldiers and Marines, after engaging in hand-to-hand combat with the enemy, froze in their sweat before they could change clothing. And always there was the horrible spectacle of frostbite of human limbs; swollen, discolored and blistered.

The Navy set up a division hospital at Wonsan and another in the Hamhung-Hungnam area of Korea's east coast in support of the Marines. It was hoped that casualties would not be too great among the leathernecks traveling the road from Hungnam on the coast to Hamhung, to Sudong, Chinhung-ni, Koto-ri, Hagaru-ri and Yudam-ni. These towns were like black wooden beads on a string, and the string was the road, unpaved, rocky, winding up, up, up. It twisted and turned through the bare hills until it reached Hagaru-ri at the Chosin Reservoir. Its surface was frozen, crusty and barely wide enough to permit the passage of a single truck.

The Eighth Army and the Tenth Corps were sweeping up there, too, and it was hoped that the United Nations forces would break the Communists' back. Medical facilities of the Army and Navy would follow all the way, and the Air Force would evacuate the sick and wounded by air.

November 25, 1950. The great end of the war offensive began. Three American divisions and three South Korean divisions opened the attack. The First Cavalry Division, the British 27th and 29th Brigades, the Turkish Brigade and the Sixth Republic of Korea Division were held in reserve, ready to move into the attack. True, there had been three aidmen sent out the day before as replacements to the infantry battalion and companies who had run into masses of Chinese. Two medics were killed, but the third man jumped into the river and escaped. He returned to report that there were more Chinese up there than he could count. Military intelligence must have known this also, but no action was taken.

The Chinese attacked at two o'clock in the morning. It began with the far-off sound of bugles and the beat of horses hoofs as the savage Reds swarmed over the hills and crossed the Yalu River. Like a human avalanche they infiltrated behind the ROK lines and hacked the green young troops to pieces. The 38th Infantry, 3,000 men, was hit by 60,000 Chinese. The outfit was completely overrun. Few got out alive. In the aid station, the doctor who was operating was shot, as was his patient. Sergeant James Loveall, a medic, was wounded by mortar fire, but he continued working on casualties. Everyone was hit and he couldn't possibly take care of them all. There was no such thing as fighting back because the chances were greater that they would hit their own men rather than the enemy. There was not even a front line because the Chinese were everywhere. Hundreds of civilians, men, women and children trying to escape were machine-gunned by the Communists.

Loveall remembers a cave in the area. Soldiers began dragging each other into it for protection. The Chinese didn't see it, and that was the only thing that saved any of them. "There were no lights so I used my cigarette lighter. Everybody was losing blood and many died because there was no medical help. My left arm and left leg were still okay. I couldn't walk so I crawled out three or four times and dragged in wounded. Anyone who could still move crawled out to get our men. There must have been fifteen of us in that cave. . . ."

Loveall will not forget the evacuation from that hellhole. "There was a two-and-a-half-ton truck with no top. It was very cold, and there were about twenty men, lying in every direction, like cord wood, piled on, or thrown onto the back of the truck. It was either that, or be left behind." The medic, though wounded twice himself, still had his aid kit so he gave everyone on the truck a shot of morphine. "The collecting station and battalion aid station had been overrun, so we traveled for three hours over the rough road until we reached the clearing station. They couldn't take care of all the casualties there so the men had to be evacuated to a MASH hospital. . . ." Meanwhile, in the darkness, casualties were mounting by the hundreds.*

Within forty-eight hours, the Eighth Army and the Tenth Corps were in full retreat, back over the ground they had fought so hard to gain. Casualties suffered by the Second Division and the Turks alone made it the worst Allied defeat of the war. The ROKs had officially "disintegrated."

As the great Allied offensive collapsed, General MacArthur announced in Tokyo that the United Nations forces were fighting "an entirely new war." Aeromedical evacuation had been important to the United Nations troops up to this point. Now it was vital to the very survival of the large forces trapped and retreating ahead of the Chinese avalanche.

On November 28, all medical evacuation teams at Ashiya, Japan, were dispatched to Sinanju in Korea. In the four-day period between November 26 and 30, when the exposed air field was closed, flight crews, med techs and nurses of the 801st Medical Air Evac Squadron evacuated 2,688 patients to hospitals in Japan.

They flew at all hours, around the clock, with the horrible specter of defeat below them. On the ground, mess supply and large trucks were set up as emergency hospital wards. Medics worked at a feverish speed. Some wounded had been carried as far as ten miles by their buddies. Load after load of wounded and maimed United Nations troops were hauled aboard air-evac planes. Med techs dodged snipers' bullets as

* From an interview with the author.

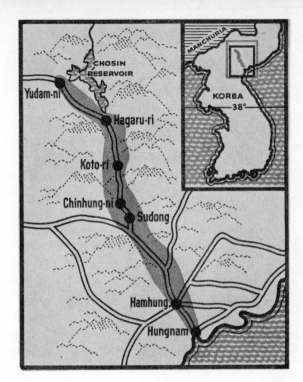

The Marines traveled the road from Hungnam on the coast to Hamhung, to Sudong, Chinhung-ni, Koto-ri, Hagaru-ri and Yudam-ni. Temperatures dropped to twenty-five degrees below zero.

they eased the litter patients out of whatever vehicles had brought them to the airstrip, treated and tagged them, secured them inside the plane, and took off.

With the Allied forces in full retreat, another crisis developed in the north. Never in United States military history were medical personnel and air-evac teams faced with a heavier responsibility or a more difficult task than when the First Marine Division, isolated at Yudam-ni, tangled with eight Chinese divisions under the command of General Sung Shin-lun.

There were 18,000 Marines holding 25 miles of road running from Chinhung-ni to Yudam-ni; 2,500 at Chinhung-ni, 3,000 in Koto-ri and another 2,500 at General H. M. Smith's headquarters at Hagaru-ri. At the top of the road in Yudam-ni were the remaining 10,000. And every one of these villages was surrounded by Chinese. In the bitter cold nights, the Communists charged, screaming "Kill! Kill!" They clanged symbols, blew whistles and shouted over loudspeakers in perfect English, "Marines, you die tonight. Your wife is lonely. Give up the fight and go home to your family."

These Chinese Communists were not the untrained rabble the Marines had defeated in 1900 during the Boxer Rebellion. They were hardened troops, whipped to a frenzy of hatred for their enemies by veterans of thirty-one years of guerrilla fighting. They avoided daylight fights that brought United States air power and artillery, and came at night, Indian style, with bayonets, potato mashers (hand grenades) and Russian guns.

They wore reversible quilted cotton uniforms and heavy cotton caps with earflaps. On their feet, they wore tennis shoes fitted over layers of heavy socks. At night, they stole Marines' clothing, especially shoes. They stripped wounded Marines, left them to freeze and shot at buddies or corpsmen crawling to rescue them.

Each Chinese carried a five-day food supply in a cloth roll slung over his shoulder. It consisted of rice, Korean millet seed, or ground peas, or a combination, which they mixed with water and ate cold or cooked. Disease and filth were rampant, and there were no real provisions for medical care. Prisoners of war, after being shaved, sprayed and de-loused, told of typhus epidemics, dysentery, even leprosy among the Communist troops. Their ages ranged from fifteen to around fifty. Wounded Communists who were captured were given medical care and were flown, via air evac, to hospitals in the rear.

The Chinese outnumbered the First Marine Division five to one. Their assignment was to *annihilate the Marines.*

The First Marine Division was the toughest, most highly motivated striking force in United States military history. For a Marine to rotate back to the States, he needed two years' overseas duty plus two Purple Hearts. Even then, he invariably chose to stay with his outfit.

Ordinarily these combat troops were clean. They used brooks, streams or portable showers for washing themselves and their clothing. They knew that a wounded man who was clean ran less danger of infection. They shaved regularly and had their hair cut by local barbers. They lived on C-rations issued daily, consisting of three cans of heavy food such as wieners and beans, hamburger in gravy or lima beans and ham. This was supplemented by bread and cookies from the bakery truck when available. There was also a can of fruit, crackers, jelly, a package of chewing gum, cigarettes and a roll of toilet paper. Ordinarily, they filled their canteens with water from mountain streams and used halizone tablets for purifying it.

At the Chosin Reservoir, icicles hung from the beards of the unshaven leathernecks. Canteens froze solid and cracked on their hips so they drank melted snow. Each man's personal weapon meant life or death. When it froze or snow was in the barrel, it was worth his life to get it into working condition. Some men, blowing into the barrel of their weapons, accidentally touched their lips to the metal and literally yanked away chunks of their own flesh. They could not dig foxholes or bunkers because the icy crusts cracked their shovels. They could not use tents for fear of giving away their positions to the enemy. The only way they could give themselves protection was to build up barriers, using snow or rocks or sandbags. They could not cook their cans of C-rations by heating them over an open fire when the temperature was twenty-five degrees below zero. The cans would burn up while the center of the food remained solid. In order to make their food edible, they melted snow in any available container and lit a fire underneath, using ammunition, toilet paper, letters from home and twigs. Then they placed the cans of food in the boiling mixture and cooked it.

The road back. Astonished Marines of the Fifth and Seventh Regiments, who hurled back a surprise onslaught by three Chinese Communist divisions, hear that they are to withdraw. In five days and nights of below-zero winds and icy roads, from November 28 to December 3, they fought back fifteen miles through Chinese hordes to Hagaru-ri, where they reorganized for the forty-mile fight down the mountain trails to the sea. They brought out their wounded and their equipment.
U.S. Marine Corps Photo

Corpsmen carried morphine and other liquid medications next to their skin to keep them from freezing. Their medical supplies were pitifully low and no one knew when, or if, more supplies would get to them.

Enemy roadblocks prevented ambulances from using the fourteen-mile mountain trail from Yudam-ni to Hagaru-ri. Marine tank and infantry patrols tried to clear the main supply route but were turned back by overwhelming enemy numbers. Ammunition was low and in some cases ran out. The Marines made their decision. They knew their only hope was to defend their positions until the separated groups could fight their way out as a division. For two days, the leathernecks presented five bristling perimeters, having no contact with one another except by air.

When they began their march back over the perilous icy road they were determined not to be a scraggly retreating bunch of beaten men. There would be no reckless dash to safety. They would stick together as a fighting outfit. But as they moved, the Chinese snapped at their flanks like jackals, their wounded stacked up, and wounded men who could not move often froze to death. They fought every inch of the way, carrying their own dead and wounded in trucks and jeeps. Corpsmen did their best to improvise ways of keeping the wounded warm, but there were not enough blankets or socks or even protective tarpaulins to go around. The ambulatories walked, and as the convoy walked, it was attacked from the hills and from roadblocks around every bend of the hideous trail. They walked night and day because to stop meant freezing to death. They walked in their sleep and awoke only when they ran into a buddy in front of them. If someone sat down or slumped into the snow, a corpsman or another Marine would slap and kick him into motion again.

Their immediate destination was Hagaru-ri, where they would reform and continue the march to the coast. This they could do, if their hundreds of wounded could be cared for.

Meanwhile, medical officers and corpsmen at Hagaru-ri anticipated the emergency of the arriving Marines, but their own medical convoy had been stopped by the enemy. Their hospital tents were crowded to overflowing. Helicopters and an L-5 flew surgical teams to Hagaru-ri and carried out the more serious cases, but this met only a fraction of the need. By November 30 there were 2,000 Marine casualties. The number increased to 3,000 when three battalions of the Seventh Infantry Division were cut off east of the reservoir.

The only hope was airlift. If they could be relieved of their wounded, the Marines coming in could continue the long icy march to Hungnam. If not, they were not sure what would happen.

But could the C-47 land on the hastily built airstrip? Thousands of lives depended on this initial landing.

Out of the gray snow-filled clouds the plane came. When the wheels touched the runway it seemed like a miracle. Throats choked with relief when the C-47 slowed down and stopped just short of the runway's end. The first twenty-four wounded Marines were readied for air evac.

This landing launched one of the most prodigious air evacs of casualties in military history. Navy surgeons and corpsmen along with Air Force med techs worked at a furious speed as the crusty little airstrip boiled with activity. By dusk, 450 casualties were evacuated to the division hospital at Hungnam, where an Air Force plane would carry them to Japan. Some were flown to the Navy hospital ship U.S.S. *Consolation*, which sat in the harbor at Hungnam. The next day, the number was doubled, and on December 3, 929 wounded or frostbitten soldiers of the Seventh Infantry Division were evacuated. Now, at last, the medics were ready for the Marines from the reservoir when they got there.

Meanwhile, the Marines slowly fought their way through the traceless wastes of snowdrifts and boulders and struggled up mountainsides to drive back the Chinese. On the night of December 1, the First Battalion of the Seventh Marines took an "impossible" route across the mountaintops to relieve Fox Company and secure the critical pass near Chinhung-ni.

With Fox Company's casualties, the few heated ambulances were jammed full. Corpsmen gave the wounded first aid, placed them in sleeping bags and lashed them to trucks. Every

U.S.S. *Repose* received casualties from Marine amphibious crafts even in rough weather during the Korean conflict. December, 1950. *U.S. Navy Photo*

inch of space on the vehicles was occupied as the head of the column wound its way into Hagaru-ri on the afternoon of December 3, carrying its 2,400 wounded men.

Not a heart remained unstirred as the column slogged into Hagaru-ri. No one knows where they found the strength to sing, but they did. "From the halls of Montezuma. . ."

Warming tents and food and medical aid were waiting for them. Whole blood, antibiotics, litters and blankets were air-dropped by C-119s while C-47s continued to shuttle the wounded out by air. By December 8, 4,689 sick and wounded men had been flown to safety from the crude airstrips at Hagaru-ri and Koto-ri.

Medical officers and corpsmen marched out of Hagaru-ri with the last troops. The Chinese occupied the perimeter and air-strip they had failed to take by assault.

The worst was over on December 10 when the column reached the foot of the mountains, and the next day the First Marine Division was in the warming tents at Hamhung. Now began the amphibious operation in reverse, which ended on Christmas Eve with the successful redeployment by Task Force 90 of all United Nations troops in Northeast Korea.

Since November 29 of that horrible winter, Marine casualties totaled 7,350, including 4,675 who were evacuated by air.

Probably the best way to find out what the troops in Korea thought of their medics and corpsmen was to ask those dazed men who lay quietly in their bunks, writing letters or staring blankly overhead, watching smoke curl up from their cigarettes. They wanted to forget what happened to them, what caused them to be brought to this place where somebody was going to try to patch them up. But their "docs," that was something else. They remembered them well.

". . .I'd like to get the name of the corpsman who saved my life. Our tank was burning and all the crew but me were killed.

I was shot through the shoulder and pinned under the tank. They were pouring machine-gun stuff at me and it was only because I was low under the tank that they didn't knock me off. This here corpsman runs up the hill with the enemy fire giving him everything, but he digs me out and drags me back. When we are safe I ask him his name and start to thank him. He said, 'Don't bother me. There's another poor s.o.b. shot up on the other side of the hill.' Then he runs back through the machine-gun country...."

Another wounded man said, "I saw a medic with his finger half blown off put a tourniquet on his wrist and then go about helping two guys with his good hand. There's no medal high enough for those guys. They should have a double Medal of Honor...."

Another. "We give the corpsmen a bad time in peace, calling them pill rollers and pot jugglers, but we respect them. They are quiet birds and shy as the devil, but what a job they do in combat."

"... We lost thirty men in our outfit and five of them were corpsmen...."

Major Stanley Wawrzyniak, "Ski" for short, has been in the United States Marine Corps since he was twenty-one years old. He has two Navy Crosses, a Silver Star and three Purple Hearts. "In combat, *everybody* knows the corpsmen. Hopefully, you get two per platoon. You take them for granted until you get into trouble."

Ski remembers the two corpsmen they had when he was with Fox Company, Fifth Marines, from January to July 1952. "Corpsman Arnold had got a Silver Star on his first tour. He had been wounded at the Chosin Reservoir but he continued on with the company. He was a funny little guy, clean-living and soft-spoken. He never swore or used rough language. He was saving his money to be a farmer.

"The other corpsman was a crybaby, always complaining

about something or other. We didn't know what to expect of him, but when the going got rough he really pitched in.

"Of course these two corpsmen were surrounded by combat-hardened Marines. It wasn't easy for them, but they fitted right in. I remember one patrol we went on and as usual, one of the corpsmen, Arnold I think it was, volunteered to go along. One of the Marines stepped on a mine and both legs were blown off. Arnold did a tremendous job of first aid and kept the boy from going into shock. He got him on a stretcher and back to an area where he could be evacuated by helicopter. He was the only corpsman there, so he was working all alone, but he managed to keep the boy alive for four hours until he could be evacuated.

"Incidentally, the boy was fitted with artificial legs and is now a floor walker in a Los Angeles department store."

Marines get to know the corpsmen attached to other companies also. Ski remembers HM1 "Obie" O'Brien, in Easy Company. "He was a registered pharmacist and was always 'tore up' because when he'd hear a call for help, he'd race through the branches and thickets. His clothes were always messed up and in tatters. The minute he'd hear a shot, he'd be on his way to find out if he was needed. . . ."*

Major Frank Colleton, USMC, was in Korea between September 1952 and July 1953 with the First Marine Division, First Regiment, Fox Company, on the west coast near Panmunjom. Of the corpsmen, he says, "On many occasions, they out-Marine a Marine. They are outstanding in their devotion to duty and their willingness to do anything you ask them to do. For instance, in a rifle platoon, there must be a patrol every night but a corpsman is always needed. The marines can rotate and take turns, but with only two corpsmen, they sometimes had to go out every night or at best every other night.

"One of our corpsmen was HM1 Simon. He wanted to be a

---

* From an interview with the author.

doctor someday. He was rosy-cheeked, completely nonathletic and it was hard to see how he ever got through boot camp. But he was a good man, a good fighter too. He carried a carbine [M-2] and pitched in when there was a fight. Such engagements were brief, maybe five to fifteen minutes. When the fighting was over and the others moved on, he stayed behind and tended the wounded.

"He wanted to belong, to be a Marine, so maybe that's why he exceeded himself. . . ."

Frank Colleton has good reason to respect corpsmen. In one engagement while on patrol, he was blinded. He couldn't possibly have found his way to safety if a corpsman hadn't turned up to carry him back to the MLR (main line of resistance). "With me on his shoulders he was a sitting duck. He couldn't hit the deck or defend himself in any way." A helicopter carried Frank Colleton to the hospital ship, where he was given definitive care for his wounds. His eyesight was completely restored.*

Lieutenant Colonel Stanley Rauh, USMC, was in command of a machine-gun and rifle platoon during action on the hook on October 26 and 27, 1952. An estimated 12,000 Chinese and North Korean troops were determined to penetrate the Marine rifle company of 300 men. The fighting was fierce. Two outposts were overrun and still the enemy came.

Stanley Rauh was in the reserve area at the time, and he was given the mission of sealing off the penetration. He moved his platoon forward through the incoming artillery and mortar fire. Casualties were intensely heavy, and Rauh himself was wounded by Willie Peter (white phosphorous from a 105 artillery shell, which the North Koreans had captured from the United States Army; the chemical burns very strongly, can melt metal and even burned the wedding band from Rauh's finger). It was terrifying because he could smell his own flesh burning.

* From an interview with the author.

Even so, the corpsman was caring for a buddy who was hurt more seriously. "There were forty-three thousand rounds of incoming artillery in a twenty-four-hour period, the greatest in military history." Another corpsman turned up and put copper sulphate gauze on Rauh's burns and got him to an area where he could be evacuated.

Colonel Rauh has three Purple Hearts for his action in Korea. Each time he recovered from a wound he went back to battle. In a later action he was hit by mortar fragmentation on a hill position where only twenty-two Marines out of fifty-five remained in action. Everyone was wounded. The situation was so critical they were told to pull back. A young Marine had to be told to pick up his rifle and move.

"I can't," he replied. "I'm hit!"

"Don't be silly. We're all hit!"

Colonel Rauh says, "I will always remember the corpsmen at the aid station playing father, mother, and sister to the wounded men. There was a doctor there who worked twenty-eight straight hours with only a coffee break. . . ."*

The war raged on, month after agonizing month. On November 1, 1952, Lieutenant General Lewis Walt, USMC, arrived with the Fifth Marines to defend the line at Panmunjom. On March 26, 1953, just before the truce, the Communists were fighting fiercely to get as much territory as possible before settlement was made. "We had trenches along the MLR. Ideally we would have had a forward element of defense also, but in this case we didn't have enough forces. There were only five thousand men to defend seven miles. So we used 'fists,' or outposts, usually located on hills that overlooked the terrain—Carson, Reno, Vegas—to warn the MLR of a mass attack. Each outpost had one officer and thirty men.

* From an interview with the author.

"On the night of March 26, the enemy opened up all they had. In forty-eight hours we received eighty thousand rounds of mortar and artillery, but fortunately we were dug into the bunkers so our casualties were light at the MLR. Then the enemy started after the outposts. By midnight they were sending a full battalion of seven or eight thousand men after an outpost of thirty men. They laid bamboo ladders over the barbed wire and overran each outpost. We sent reinforcements out but because the area was mined, they had to stick to the trails. Reno was in a bad way. All but five of our men were killed. Since it was a mile and a half away, our machine guns were not effective and the enemy had it completely surrounded. There were about two thousand Chinese in the Reno area and the relief platoon was stopped. I sent another one hundred and fifty men to reinforce the platoon, but by the time they got there about half of the platoon was either dead or wounded. Among them was a hospital corpsman named Francis Hammond.

"Hammond had sustained a leg wound, but he had patched himself up and was crawling around taking care of the wounded. Our men fought for four hours, trying to get to Reno, but it was impossible. They sustained about thirty-five percent casualties and many were dead. I finally decided to pull the company back. We covered them with heavy fire as they brought their dead and wounded with them.

"Hammond refused to go back with the first of the wounded. He continued to drag himself around to look after the Marines. He was shot again through the side and was knocked down. A few minutes later he patched himself up and was back at it. When the company finally came out, Hammond hobbled out with them. Just as he got inside our own lines, he stepped on a mine and was killed. That boy saved a lot of Marines that night. . . ."*

* From an interview with the author.

Francis Hammond was awarded the Medal of Honor (post-humous). A new high school in the young corpman's home-town of Alexandria, Virginia, is named in his honor.

With all the care medics give to others, one can imagine how things go when one of their own is brought in to the aid station.

Fred Wolf was nineteen at the time he arrived in Korea in September 1951 as a replacement medic in the Seventh Cavalry, First Division. His platoon was ordered to go up and occupy a knoll. It was November 10 at nine o'clock in the morning, and the Chinese were throwing everything at them: mortars, small-arms and machine-gun fire.

Wolf's platoon scattered to the far side of the knoll in order to get away from the machine-gun fire, but as they ran, his buddy was hit. Wolf stopped to take care of him, then yelled for a cou-ple of G.I.s to carry the litter to a trench where he'd be safe. There, Fred gave the man morphine and managed to stop the bleeding. Suddenly he heard a crash and then his ears began ringing. He smelled smoke, and could even taste the gun-powder. Blood began gushing out of his mouth. A Chinese high-fragmentation mortar had hit Fred in the right chest, both arms and legs, ankle and top of his right arm.

The platoon sergeant appeared, put his rubber raincoat down on the ground, got Fred into it, gathered up the four corners and dragged him off the ridge. Four other G.I.s came over. Each man grabbed a corner of the raincoat and carried him to the aid station. Fred showed them how to give him a shot of morphine for the two-and-a-half-hour trip.

It was Fred's own aid station, and his own medics looked after him. "I remember there were four of them working on me at the same time."

The list of heroes is a long one—as long as more than a thou-sand days of combat in Korea, as long as one terrible night on the outpost line of resistance. . .

MEDAL OF HONOR (posthumous)

David Richard DeWert, Hospitalman, USN, served as a medical corpsman with a Marine infantry company, First Marine Division, during action against enemy aggressor forces in Korea on April 5, 1951. When a fire team from the point platoon of his company was pinned down by a deadly barrage of hostile automatic-weapons fire and suffered many casualties, DeWert rushed to the assistance of one of the more seriously wounded and, despite a painful leg wound sustained while dragging the stricken Marine to safety, steadfastly refused medical treatment for himself and immediately dashed back through the fireswept area to carry a second wounded man out of the line of fire. Undaunted by the mounting hail of devastating enemy fire, he bravely moved forward a third time and received another serious wound in the shoulder after discovering that a wounded Marine had already died. Still persistent in his refusal to submit to first aid, he resolutely answered the call of a fourth stricken comrade and, while rendering medical assistance, was himself mortally wounded by a burst of enemy fire. He gallantly gave his life for his country.

MEDAL OF HONOR (posthumous)

Hospital Corpsman Third Class Edward Clyde Benfold, USN, was twenty-one years old at the time he served as a hospital corpsman with the First Marine Division in Korea on September 5, 1952. When his company was subjected to heavy artillery and mortar barrages, followed by a determined assault during the hours of darkness by an enemy force estimated at battalion strength, Benfold resolutely moved from position to position in the face of intense hostile fire, treating the wounded and lending words of encouragement. Leaving the protection of his sheltered position to treat the wounded when the platoon area in which he was working was attacked from both the front and rear, he moved forward to an exposed ridge line where he observed two Marines in a large crater. As he approached the two men to determine their condition, an enemy soldier threw two grenades into the crater while two other enemy soldiers charged the position. Picking up a grenade in each hand, Benfold leaped out of the crater and hurled himself against the onrushing hostile soldiers, pushing the grenades against their chests and killing both the attackers. Mortally wounded while carrying out this heroic act, Benfold, by his great personal valor and resolute spirit of self-sacrifice in the face of almost certain death, was directly responsible for saving the lives of his two comrades. He gallantly gave his life for others.

MEDAL OF HONOR (posthumous)

Hospitalman John Edward Kilmer, USN, served as a medical corpsman with a Marine rifle company in the First Marine Division during action against the enemy in Korea on August 13, 1952. With his company engaged in defending a vitally important hill position well forward of the main line of resistance during an assault by large concentrations of hostile troops, Kilmer repeatedly braved intense enemy mortar, artillery and sniper fire to move from one position to another, administering aid to the wounded and expediting their evacuation. Painfully wounded himself when struck by mortar fragments while moving to the aid of a casualty, he persisted in his efforts and inched his way to the side of the stricken Marine through a hail of enemy shells falling around him. Undaunted by the devastating hostile fire, he skillfully administered first aid to his comrade and, as another mounting barrage of enemy fire shattered the immediate area, unhesitatingly shielded the wounded man with his own body. Kilmer was mortally wounded by flying shrapnel while carrying out this heroic action. He gallantly gave his life for another.

MEDAL OF HONOR (posthumous)

Private First Class Bryant H. Womack, USA, served with the Medical Company, 14th Infantry Regiment, 25th Infantry Division, during action against the enemy on March 12, 1952, near Sokso-ri, Korea. PFC Womack was the only medical aidman attached to a night combat patrol when sudden contact with a numerically superior enemy produced many casualties. Womack immediately went to their aid, although this necessitated exposing himself to a devastating hail of enemy fire, during which he was seriously wounded. Refusing medical aid for himself, he continued moving among his comrades to administer aid. While he was aiding one man, he was again struck by enemy mortar fire, this time suffering the loss of his right arm. Although he knew the consequences of not treating his wounds, he insisted that all efforts be directed toward helping the other casualties. Although unable to perform the task himself, he remained on the scene and directed others in first-aid techniques. The last man to withdraw, he walked until he collapsed from loss of blood, and died a few minutes later while being carried by his comrades.

MEDAL OF HONOR

Sergeant David B. Bleak was a farmer in Idaho before he enlisted in the Army to become an aidman. In Korea, he was a member of the Medical Company, 223d Infantry Regiment, 40th Infantry Division, and he distinguished himself during action against the enemy in the vicinity of Minari-gol on June 14, 1952. As a medical aidman, he volunteered to accompany a reconnaissance patrol committed to engaging the enemy and capturing a prisoner for interrogation. Forging up the rugged slope of the key terrain, the group was subjected to intense automatic-weapons and small-arms fire and suffered several casualties. After administering to the wounded, Bleak continued to advance with the patrol. Nearing the military crest of the hill, while attempting to cross the fireswept area to attend the wounded, he came under hostile fire from a small group of the enemy concealed in a trench. Entering the trench, he closed with the enemy, killed two with his bare hands and a third with his trench knife. Moving from the emplacement, he saw a concussion grenade fall in front of a companion and, quickly shifting his position, shielded the man from the impact of the blast. Later, while administering to the wounded, he was struck by a hostile bullet but, despite the wound, he undertook to evacuate a wounded comrade. As he moved down the hill with his heavy burden, he was attacked by two enemy soldiers with fixed bayonets. Closing with the aggressors, he grabbed them and smashed their heads together, then carried his helpless comrade down the hill to safety.

10

Vietnam

$\mathbb{A}$ few days before Christmas in 1961, a young American, Specialist 4 James T. Davis of Livingston, Tennessee, was riding in a "deuce and a half" truck along with ten Vietnamese soldiers. The roadside seemed clear enough of dangerous foliage that could hide the Vietcong. At this particular stretch, there were no sharp curves around which the enemy could be expected to ambush. Suddenly, with no warning, a huge blast erupted from a mound of earth at the side of the road. The truck was crushed like a toy, and bloody troops were strewn in all directions. Davis landed in a ditch, still clutching his carbine. He managed to empty two magazines of cartridges at the attackers. But the Vietcong had machine guns. On December 22, 1961, Specialist Davis became the first American serviceman to die in combat with the Vietcong.

Young Davis' death by ambush is symbolic of the kind of dirty, dangerous, frustrating and confusing war that Americans are fighting in Vietnam. Although the United States has fought in two world wars and again in Korea, most military experience is inapplicable in this small Southeast Asian hotbed.

The French know this; they battled—and finally lost out to— the Indochinese rebels for nearly a decade. In 1954 they made peace with the Vietminh at a Geneva parley during which Indochina was cut into four independent parts: Laos, Cambodia, and the two parts of Vietnam (the northern half a Communist state and the southern half eventually becoming a relatively free state).

By 1957 and 1958, the South Vietnamese government found itself fighting another kind of war against the guerrilla Communists in the mountains and in the swampy delta country south of Saigon. It was countryman against countryman and often one family member against another. In Washington, President Eisenhower said that if South Vietnam should fall to the Communists, all of Southeast Asia would collapse like a house of cards. President Kennedy in 1961 sent General Maxwell Taylor to South Vietnam as a military adviser to assess the danger of Communism. Interim aid of various sorts was given the South Vietnamese government, and in December 1961, the first American helicopter outfit, the 57th Transport Helicopter Company, arrived to bring the assistance of vertical envelopment to the South Vietnamese troops, lifting them into battle against the Vietcong. Soon, other helicopter units arrived; American advisory units were increased and antiguerrilla training programs were stepped up. In January 1962, the United States Military Advisory Command, Vietnam (USMACV) under General Paul Harkins was set up. American Special Forces troops began to arrive in Vietnam. With them came their highly skilled, cross-trained medics.

Master Sergeant Hobart Nantz, E-8, was a Ranger Trainer attached to the Ranger Training Center in Trung-lap from November 1961 to June 1962. From June to November 1962 he served with the Tenth Special Forces Battalion. The blond, thirty-two-year-old medic was an ideal choice for the sensitive job he would hold as the first American medic to serve with the advisory team. His sixteen years of service had all been with the medics except for one tour in Japan with the combat engineers. He was airborne, in top physical condition and carried top-secret clearance. He was cross-trained in weapons, communications and demolition. "We needed a working knowledge of just about every phase of the Vietnamese operation. . . ."

Nantz's mission was to provide medical aid to American officers and men. But he was also assigned the job of teaching Vietnamese Ranger medics the basic fundamentals of sanitation, hygiene and first aid. Whenever possible, he was to set up a kind of first-aid station in each village and hamlet, select and

Sergeant Hobert Nantz, Chief Wardmaster at the U.S. Army Hospital in Heidelberg, Germany, was the first medic to serve with the advisory teams in Vietnam. Photo shows him examining a foot injury caused by a Vietcong spike.

train local citizens to maintain it and check back periodically to see that it was being run properly.

"It is difficult to teach someone to become a medic who has no knowledge whatsoever of our standard of hygiene or living. You start with nothing—a fellow who has been a farmer and has lived all of his life in a primitive village—and you try to teach him how to take care of himself and others.

"Since sanitation was so poor, I tried to teach them about fly control. They laughed at me because they could not understand how a little fly could be dangerous. There were no toilets; food was always left uncovered. Their personal hygiene was bad, so I taught them about washing their armpits and bodies. There was no point in telling them to change their socks because they didn't wear socks and of course they had no soap...."

"It was hard to overcome their old beliefs. Even educated commanding officers believed in the old tales. They were convinced that headaches were caused by evil spirits and the only cure was to pinch their foreheads and pull the evil spirit out. Many Vietnamese troops were going around with huge blood blisters on their foreheads as a result of this 'home cure.'

"They believed in the sympathetic treatment of injuries. If one leg is hurt, you treat the other one. That will make the bad one heal."

The Vietnamese do not have cooks assigned as do the American forces. Instead, each person is given his ration of rice, which he proceeds to cook. Sergeant Nantz taught the troops and the medics not to throw their refuse near wells where it could contaminate the water. They agreed to this, but, as so often happened, when Nantz returned at a later time to visit, he found them using the same old procedures.

Nantz observed that Army of the Republic of Vietnam medics carried their casualties in a net with a pole stuck through it. In this crumpled-up position, the patient was dragged over rice paddies and rough terrain, all of which did more harm than good. He taught them the proper way of transporting the sick and wounded by improvising a litter from a poncho or blanket and bamboo poles. He also showed them how to use a pistol strap to carry a man out of a battle zone. He moved on with his unit, but when he returned, the Vietnamese medics were back to the same old net, with one pole. ARVN medics are now being sent to medical school in Saigon. In the meantime, in actual operation, if a Vietnamese medic is hit, he turns his bag over to another man and says, "You're the new medic!"

In the villages and hamlets, Sergeant Nantz held sick call for the natives. Many had never seen Western medicine of any sort before, and since the young medic had never been given any definite guidelines on what he should do in treating these people, he decided to do what he must. Often there would be 200 to 300 people lined up to see him with all manner of injuries and diseases resulting from malnutrition and filth.

"They all responded well to antibiotics. I gave them vitamin pills for malnutrition, aspirin for headaches and passed out the worm medicine."

Nantz arranged for an ARVN medic to come into the villages and inoculate the people against smallpox and typhoid. "We probably treated and vaccinated a lot of Vietcong in the process. . . ."

As a member of the advisory team, Sergeant Nantz lived and fought with the South Vietnamese troops. He got used to eating rice that had been cooked the day before, because often it was too dangerous to build fires that would reveal their position. "You just roll the rice into a ball and eat it." There was no such thing as K- or C-rations. American advisers wearing jungle fatigues and red berets lived on fruit and wildlife from the jungle. It was impossible to keep fresh meat more than two days, so the medic from Kentucky found himself carrying a live chicken or duck attached to his belt and feeding it for four or five days before eating it. Sometimes they strapped on a ham from a freshly killed pig "captured" in a Vietcong village.

In this different kind of war, the American medic wore rubber bands around his trouser legs to keep out the leeches that infested every swamp. Even so, troops stopped every two or three hours to "de-leech." He slept in a jungle hammock or in a villager's hut on top of a hard wooden table.

Seasoned American advisers traveled light. Usually Nantz carried his medical supplies, a change of underwear and, if it were to be a long operation, a change of jungle fatigues. His weapons consisted of an infantry carbine and grenades, but he was trained and experienced in all types of weapons: Swedish Ks, Belgium twelve-gauge shotguns, AR-15s, machine guns, mortars, BARs (Browning), Thompson submachine guns and unconventional guerrilla hand weapons.

The weather was hot, sticky and mucky, and Nantz often found himself treating a newcomer for heat exhaustion. At noon, when the sun was like a hot blast furnace, everyone rested for two hours. "Americans think they can keep right on going, but they soon learn differently. The VC would make their observations in the daytime, then attack at night. That's why both the VC and the ARVN troops kept on the move."

Living, fighting and working with the Vietnamese, Sergeant Nantz learned about the new kind of war and the Communist Vietcong.

"The VC wear black pajamas, like those of the peasants, so it is often impossible to tell friend from foe. Sometimes they even dress in women's clothes. They are masters of camouflage. Their helmets, made of wicker and plastic sheeting, look like inverted pie tins. They swathe their entire bodies in foliage which they change often as they move across the terrain.

"Their weapons were equally 'nonregulation.' Sometimes they consisted of old French firearms or captured American carbines.

They fashioned their own knives and manufactured their hand grenades and grenade launchers in hidden jungle factories. Many VC used the mountain crossbow, which is two and a half feet long and requires a pull of one hundred pounds to cock its leather string. They made their shoes from American-made tire inner tubes."

As a medic, Nantz picked up thousands of foot spikes, which he sent to Japan for study. "These spikes, which the VC stuck into concrete or wooden blocks, were designed to penetrate the foot, even through heavy G.I. boots, of anyone who stepped on them. Medical intelligence revealed that the spikes had been contaminated."

The VC also put up bamboo spikes in pits, staggered six to eight inches apart. These traps were usually found near the ventilation holes of the tunnels. "The VC had a vast network of tunnels interconnected in a huge maze with camouflaged holes extending to the surface every five feet or so. Poisonous vipers were often put into the pits, along with the spikes. Mines, booby traps and snipers were invariably posted at tunnel entrances and ventilation holes. . . .

"The system of taking a Vietcong village was called 'blocking and sweeping.' One company would set it up and another would sweep through. But every village had tunnels, and the VC knew where the pits and mines were. Anyone going after them would fall into the pits. The tunnels were ingenious. For instance, if you were looking down into a well into which a VC had disappeared, all you could see was muddy water. But down there was a trap door out of which the enemy could escape to safety. A smoke bomb or hand grenade would not touch them. The VC can stay underwater for hours, breathing through a hollow reed.

"Sneak terror attacks and ambushes were among their favorite forms of attack. After an ambush we never knew how many VC had been killed because they carried off their dead and wounded or quickly buried them in holes they had dug before the ambush. We could see trails of blood and grooves in the dirt from the man's heels. . . ."*

The American advisers, men like Sergeant Nantz, were a special breed of servicemen. Until March 1965, they were the backbone of the United States military effort in Vietnam and, as Ambassador Henry Cabot Lodge said of them, "something brave and noble is going on out there. . . ."

Even now, with pockets like Danang, Camranh, Bienhoa and Vungtao near Saigon filled with thousands of soldiers and Marines, more than 5,000 advisers still remain; teaching, suggesting, guiding, cajoling and fighting for their lives at any moment of the day or night. These are the men possessing the guts of a lion and the patience of Job, identifying with the little South Vietnamese soldier whose country they assist. The greatest single virtue of the advisers has been patience.

The men who have come to South Vietnam with the escalation of the war are not required to have that extra restraint and understanding that come from living and fighting with troops who are not like themselves. Most of the early advisers have moved on. Sergeant Nantz is now Chief Wardmaster at the U.S. Army Hospital in Heidelberg, Germany.

By the end of 1965, more than 200,000 were in South Vietnam (compared with 23,000 in January of that year) plus thousands more offshore with the Seventh Fleet and others in neighboring Thailand and at nearby island bases. In October 1966, 275,000 Americans were serving in South Vietnam, with 50,000 to 60,000 Navy personnel offshore. By March 1966, six corpsmen had been killed, twenty wounded. In October 1966, the total number of Americans who had died in action, of wounds, disease or accident totaled 5,302.

It has been a different, a new kind of war for the troops and strategists, but the medical departments have faced the age-

* From an interview with the author.

old problem of taking care of troops in a disease-ridden country. Dysentery, hepatitis, skin problems and a virulent form of malaria (falciparum) are the cause of about seventy-five percent of hospital admissions. From January 1961 through November 1965, 3,699 men in the Army were wounded or injured as a result of actions against hostile forces. Twenty-six of these (less than one percent) died of their wounds. A similar percentage is found with the Navy and Marine Corps.

But it is also a new kind of war for the medical departments. Their hospitals are often under attack by Vietcong terrorists. Their supplies are bottled up in the harbor because of lack of docking space. They read reports of peace marches and protests at home, and they fervently hope for peace under the right conditions—but in the meantime they concentrate on caring for the casualties.

The medical departments are much better prepared to care for American casualties in Vietnam than in any overseas war in history. There are personnel, facilities and an excellent air-evac system for the care of American military men as well as sick and injured Vietnamese civilians. As of December 1965, the Army alone had more than 1,000 Army Medical Service officers, including physicians, dentists, veterinarians, nurses and Medical Service Corps officers and over 3,000 medical aidmen in Vietnam. Army medics are now assigned to hospitals, medical helicopter evacuation units, medical units organic to combat elements and a variety of auxiliary medical units. At present, there are two evacuation hospitals, two surgical hospitals and two field hospitals in the country. These hospitals are located at Quinhon, Bienhoa, Saigon and Nhatrang.

The majority of Navy medical facilities are located in the Marine Corps areas of operation. One is the 107-bed station hospital in Saigon where nine doctors, eight nurses and eighty-four hospital corpsmen have taken care of casualties from Vietcong terrorist activities: the bombing of the Brink Hotel, the Ameri-

December 6, 1965. The Third Medical Battalion at Danang. *U.S. Marine Corps Photo*

can Embassy, the Metropole Hotel, the MyCanh Floating Restaurant and others. They also care for casualties from the battle zones, which are landed by helicopter in a nearby soccer field and transferred to a Navy ambulance that carries them to the hospital. The permanent, one-story building is nearing completion and will soon be taken over by the Army. To date they have cared for 25,000 in-patients and 53,000 out-patients, given 93,000 immunizations and filled 93,000 prescriptions. The building has an air-conditioned operating room and recovery area, vitally important in such a climate. The other hospital recently completed is located in Danang and, because it is the farthest north, has no female nurses. There are 170 doctors and 1,500 corpsmen working there.

There are four C&C company (collecting and clearing company) sixty-bed emergency surgery hospitals, which are picked up and carried off to follow the Marines in the field. These are located at Danang, Chulai, Phubai, and Quinhon. They do not, however, zigzag back and forth with each troop movement as was the case during World War II and the Korean War. Now, helicopters bring battle casualties directly from the front to the semifixed field hospital, which has the advantage of air-conditioning and more sterile facilities.

Commander Almon C. Wilson, MC, USN, reports from Headquarters, Third Medical Battalion, Third Marine Division, at Danang. "The largest numbers of corpsmen attached to the Marines are unrated men who serve at the smallest unit levels of the infantry (and other type) outfits. These are the HMs who look after their men minute by minute, in camp or in the field. They are charged with the responsibility of seeing that first aid is rendered to their wounded in the field (and the HMs go along when the particular unit to which they are attached moves out on a patrol or 'sweep'). But they also have a host of other jobs: sanitation—seeing to it that there is potable water available and, if there is none, being sure that the men are using their water-purification tablets correctly to sterilize a stream or pool of water. They make sure that there are properly placed four-holers complete with screening, etc., that food service is reasonably clean, that preventive medications are taken (malaria is the big one at the moment) and that the general welfare of the men is watched to guard against undue fatigue with all its attendant and dangerous problems; an overtired Marine on patrol is not as wary as one who has had some rest. Corpsmen must also keep the commanding officers informed of any and all problems related to their men in terms of the men's health, which in turn reflects the unit's military capability.

"Our corpsmen become air-traffic controllers when they call for a helicopter evac for a wounded man in the field. They set up an area for the helo landings and direct the choppers in on the area.

"In the normal, everyday course of their duties, they apply battle dressings to wounds, start intravenous fluids and splint fractures. They even serve as chaplains at times. There is great respect for 'the docs' in the Marine Corps, and they are cared for by their Marine charges with great consistency. The Marine feels that he may need 'the doc' any time, and he wants him all in one piece and ready to work.

"The other portion of the group assigned to the Fleet Marine Force are the rated men, most of whom are technicians. The battalion aid station has one or two general medical officers and twenty-one corpsmen, including some operating-room technicians and preventive-medicine technicians. The greatest concentration of technicians is in the C&C emergency surgery hospital, where they can function in their technical specialties such as lab, pharmacy, operating room, X-ray, preventive medicine, etc.

". . . *All* corpsmen do such things as pitch tents, dig drainage ditches and foxholes, drive ambulances, wash, clean, wrap and sterilize medical instruments and supplies, order supplies and keep logs of patients seen and patients evacuated, etc. In truth, our corpsmen 'do everything,' from running the administrative-records offices to building four-holers, to running the guard mail and post office. We have several who have been a permanent part of the perimeter security guard and spend all their duty time in foxholes guarding the perimeter at night to keep out VC probers. Some are most enterprising. One fellow runs the local laundry concession. He collects the laundry to be done, takes it to the laundry in town and retrieves it when finished. Another is a self-styled (and his style is excellent) landing control officer. And he is *always* on hand when a chopper comes in. On one particularly busy occasion he controlled over fifty helo landings in the space of five or six hours and sometimes had two on the pad at once. He is a Mexican boy from Tijuana. That same boy is also a laboratory technician who earned his designation in on-the-job training, a difficult thing to do because lab techs usually require formal training for about a year.

"Last but not least are the corpsmen who shuffle papers: the administrative men, supply clerks, evacuation control desk operators, etc. All of these jobs are handled by a strange assortment of corpsmen, some of whom by background and training have had no experience in their FMF duties. For example, the HM who runs the air-evac desk and does it with extreme competence is an X-ray technician. There is a fundamental flexibility in our HMs that bridges many practical gaps in a very down-to-earth brass-tacks function. . . ."*

The Air Force Medical Service has a 200-bed tent hospital at Camranh Bay and operates small dispensaries and out-patient

* From correspondence with the author.

Medics do what they can to ease the suffering of the Vietcong. Medic has given the fallen VC a shot of morphine and is now cutting a piece of adhesive tape to patch a bullet hole. *Department of Defense Photo*

clinics at Tansonnhut Air Field, Nhatrang Air Field, Pleiku Airport, Bienhoa, Binhthuy, Phanrang and Danang. The Air Force effort in Vietnam has been concentrated mainly on aero-medical evacuation.

Even so, business at these ground installations, is, to be blunt, often booming. For instance, the USAF dispensary at Bienhoa Air Base was only a small room in the operations building in January 1965. Today it is a ten-room facility where electro-cardiograms, bacteriological cultures, blood counts and serologi-cal studies can be performed. It receives over 2,000 patients a month for regular sick call and emergencies. Included are physi-cals performed on civilian Vietnamese who work at the base, support of Army and other military units and a medical team that makes weekly visits to treat Vietnamese children in the local area.

TSgt. Claude H. McKinnon serves as a flight-medicine tech-nician. It is his job to see that air-crew effectiveness is main-tained. He, like all the medical technicians, doubles on sick call and in other departments. "The work load is heavy enough for twice the number of people, but none of us minds," he says.

At Bienhoa, as everywhere, there are the Vietcong. "I was on duty about twelve-oh-five A.M. on November 1, when the mortar shells began going off. I changed from whites to fatigues and reported back to the dispensary annex, which we then moved to the dining hall to set up an emergency dispensary. We began handling emergency cases all over the place, one at the canton-ment gate—but we took care of all of them—evacuated a good many to Saigon. We finally got through with it all around three-thirty P.M."

McKinnon's assistant in the treatment room, A1C Joseph Nash, was one of those cited for bravery during the May 16 bomb explosions. He and Staff Sergeants Anthony Beasley, Billy Carrico and William Milner received the Airman's Medal for heroism during the tragedy. Typical of the medics, they

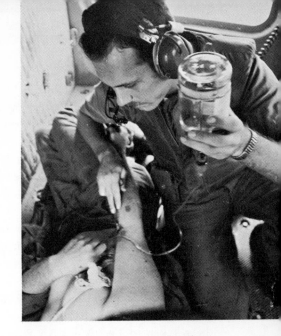

HM2 Fred E. Davis, United States Navy corpsman assigned to medical evacuations with Marine helicopters at Danang, administers to a wounded Marine en route to a field hospital. "Doc" Davis may treat a dozen wounded men that his copter has taken out of firefights during a 24-hour tour of watch. *U.S. Marine Corps Photo*

repeatedly entered the fireswept area to rescue and treat victims. Carrico suffered a shrapnel wound in the knee while rescuing victims of the blast but continued with his work.

Flying medics of the USAF's aeromedical-evacuation system are writing a fantastic chapter in the history of military medicine. As in the past two wars, they have taken to the skies in their airborne hospitals to care for thousands of sick and wounded men en route to hospitals located away from the battle zones.

How does the system work?

Take a G.I. named Joe—or he could be a sailor, Marine or airman. It doesn't matter because regardless of what service he is in the combined efforts of the medical departments will look after him. But let's say Joe was with an airborne platoon that was trying to take a Vietcong position north of Saigon. He was lying there alternately hugging the ground and inching forward when he was hit by mortar fire. And that's all he remembered for a while. Then the aidman was bandaging him up and giving him a shot of morphine and setting up an IV. His mind began to clear as he heard the whirring chop-chop of the helicopter's rotors. He watched as it settled nicely into the cleared area and wondered vaguely if any VC snipers would take a potshot at it. This time it escaped any murderous groundfire, and soon he and five other litter patients were expertly loaded aboard the UH-1D. Once secured, they took off again. In addition to the six wounded litter patients, there were two aviators (pilot and copilot), an aircrew chief and a medical airman aboard.

About an hour later, the helicopter settled down on a field beside a hospital. Here Joe was treated by a physician and prepared for further evacuation in a Pacific Air Force (PACAF) C-118 air-evac plane to the new 300-bed Air Force hospital at Clark Air Base in the Philippines. He could, of course, have been taken to Tachikawa Air Base in Japan or Kadena Air Base in Okinawa where the Military Airlift Command (MAC) C-141 jets fly patients across the big water to Tripler Hospital in Hawaii or to the mainland. There are a number of specialized hospitals in the United States such as the Brook Army Medical Center in San Antonio where burns are best treated, or Walter Reed Hospital, considered best for amputation, or one of several Air Force specialty centers. The Clark Air Base hospital itself specializes in casualties who have suffered chest and spinal wounds.

Air evac plays an increasingly important role in saving lives and alleviating pain. Its worldwide score for the first nine months of 1965 reached a whopping 58,975; within Southeast Asia, a total of 11,994 sick and wounded had been transported in this manner.

Where World War II and Korean War air evac was slow and ponderous with hours and hours spent in the air during the long overwater flights, today's improved aircraft carry patients quickly and comfortably over vast distances of the globe. Patients can be delivered to the hospital at Clark Air Base within five hours from the time they were wounded. In nineteen to twenty hours, they can be carried from the battlefield in Vietnam to the hospital at Travis Air Force Base in California.

As medical care for the serviceman has improved in the air-evac system, so has the Navy ushered in a whole new era of medical care afloat, with the hospital ship U.S.S. *Repose.* The concept of a floating hospital that can be underway to an area in need of help within a few hours is not a new one. Commo-

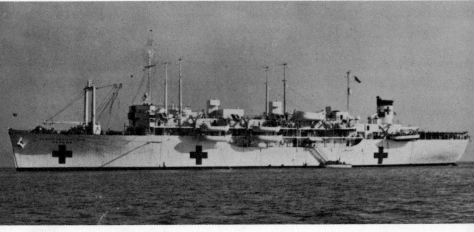

250 Navy corpsmen serve aboard the recently refurbished Navy hospital ship U.S.S. *Repose* (AH-16) in the Vietnam area. *U.S. Navy Photo*

dore Preble gave the American Navy its first hospital ship during the war with Tripoli. The U.S.S. *Intrepid* served in that capacity for two months before she was returned to the line. The *Red Rover*, which served during the Civil War, is perhaps the most famous of the early hospital ships. World War II produced a fleet of eighteen hospital ships, three of which also served during the Korean War: the *Repose*, the *Consolation* and the *Haven.* Each of these ships was equipped with a helicopter

Aboard the Navy hospital ship U.S.S. *Repose*, a helicopter brings a casualty for fast, definitive treatment. March, 1966. *U.S. Navy Photo*

Captain Theodore Wilson, MC, USN, the *Repose's* chief surgeon, puts his ear close to a wounded Marine. All wounded are brought to this tri-age station where their wounds are diagonosed and logged. They are then sent to the proper operating room or medical ward for treatment. *U.S. Navy Photo* landing platform so that casualties could be flown directly from the battlefront to a floating hospital facility where they received definitive medical and surgical care, frequently only twenty or thirty minutes after they were wounded. Following cessation of hostilities in Korea, these ships were put into the "mothball" fleet.

With the escalation of the war in Southeast Asia, the *Repose* was again pressed into service. Beginning in the summer of 1965 she was ordered out of the Suisun Bay mothball fleet for a $9,000,000 face-lifting, and today she is truly a modern diagnostic and treatment facility. Her helicopter pad can receive the heavier craft now in use. If weather precludes patient transportation by air, ambulatory patients can come aboard by way of one of four ladders, and electrically driven hoists bring litter patients aboard.

Staffing the 750-bed hospital are 24 physicians, 3 dentists, 7 Medical Service Corps officers, 2 chaplains, 29 nurses and 250 hospital corpsmen and dental technicians.

In addition to providing the basic facilities and capabilities of a large modern hospital, the *Repose* carries several innovations to front-line diagnosis and treatment. For years the Navy has pioneered in the preservation of blood by freezing. As yet they have not used frozen blood in Vietnam, but the *Repose* does have the capability for storing and reconstituting frozen blood. Frozen blood can be stored for an indefinite period of time and reconstituted, ready for use, within a matter of minutes.

The ship carries a portable pump-oxygenator and an artificial heart, with trained personnel to utilize them. Vice Admiral Robert B. Brown, Surgeon General of the Navy, explains, "The feasibility and importance of repairing damaged blood vessels in the arms and legs in forward medical facilities was definitely established during the Korean War. We believe it should now be determined whether a front-line capability to support the circulation of the patient artificially and to do direct surgery on

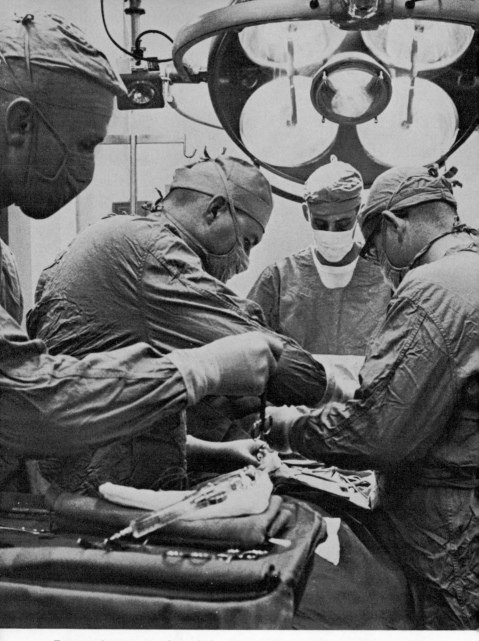

Teams of surgeons aboard the U.S.S. *Repose* often work on several areas of the wounded man's body simultaneously. *U.S. Navy Photo*

the heart (and the large vessels connected to it) is also important...."

Aboard the *Repose* is the most modern laboratory equipment. Included in the advanced diagnostic techniques available is the one which utilizes an antigen-antibody reaction and a fluorescent dye to identify rapidly the causitive organism of such diseases as tuberculosis and malaria. There is an artificial kidney aboard ship which can be used when kidney failure occurs following an attack of malaria similar to black-water fever.

Located beneath the helipad is a recompression chamber. This chamber can be used for treatment of flying and diving casualties and also for providing oxygen under pressure for the treatment of certain types of infection including tetanus and gas gangrene.

But what of the people-to-people work?

Lieutenant General Lewis Walt, who earlier described his experiences with corpsmen during World War II Pacific campaigns and in Korea and who now commands the Marines in Vietnam, says, "Taking real estate is just the beginning. Next you've somehow got to win over the hearts and minds of the populace...."

This is what today's corpsmen and medics are doing by volunteering their special skills in a variety of ways to the desperate civilians of South Vietnam. Sometimes it is a single medic or corpsman who takes it upon himself to set up a "washbasin" clinic in a small hamlet or village where he will break out his kit to treat sores, burns, injuries or diseases. Often this is done at the risk of his life but the knowledge that he is helping others is reward enough. In addition to individual medics helping out, organized medical assistance comes from all the medical departments.

Since January 1963, medics have been working in the Military Medical Civic Action Program (MEDCAP). The primary purpose of this program is to fill the critical void of medical care

Sick call is held by corpsmen at small fishing village three miles south of Marble Mountain during Operation War Bonnet, January 3, 1966. *U.S. Marine Corps Photo*

Hospital corpsman R. C. Clay bandages a hurt knee for a small Vietnamese boy from the village of Pho Nan Thuong Ho as the boy's friends look on. All villagers were removed from the village for questioning by Vietnamese Civil Affairs soldiers during this operation. *U.S. Marine Corps Photo*

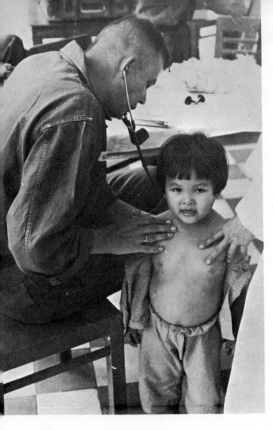

Dr. (Captain) David L. Gehlhoff examines a youngster at the My Tho orphanage during a MED-CAP visit. *Department of Defense Photo*

and treatment to people living in the rural and often isolated countryside areas. In coordination with the United States Overseas Mission (USOM) and the Minister of Health of the Republic of Vietnam, U.S. and ARVN military personnel were organized into mobile medical teams which travel to the remote villages and hamlets and provide critically needed medical care for the sick and injured. In addition, these medical teams teach and qualify local villagers as health workers so that they can establish and operate their own health stations.

Closely allied to the function of MEDCAP are the 109 United States District Advisory Teams that are located throughout most provinces of South Vietnam. These are the teams with which Sergeant Nantz served. Today, each team is staffed with two officers and three enlisted men. One of the three is a medical specialist who provides medical advice and treatment to ARVN paramilitary personnel (Civil Guard, Self Defense Corps). Whenever possible, this same medic provides medical care for the paramilitary dependents of the local village civilians.

The story of medics in Vietnam and in Southeast Asia has just begun to be written. Their jobs on land, sea and in the air continue to get tougher, more dangerous and more demanding. They require more technical skill than ever before in history. And yet, these men whose careers are dedicated to saving the lives of others must, and do, retain their traditional characteristics: dedication to duty, empathy for their fellow humans, wit, skill and guts.

BIBLIOGRAPHY

Bibliography

BOOKS

Adams, George W., *Doctors in Blue*, New York, Henry Schuman, Inc., 1952.

Ashburn, P. M., *A History of the Medical Department of the U. S. Army*, Boston, Houghton Mifflin Co., 1929.

Cunningham, H. H., *Doctors in Gray*, Baton Rouge, Louisiana, Louisiana State University Press, 1958.

Engle, Eloise, *Pararescue*, New York, The John Day Company, 1964.

Holcomb, Richard, *A Century with Norfolk Naval Hospital*, Portsmouth, Virginia, Printcraft Press, 1930.

Hume, Edgar E., *Victories of Army Medicine*, Philadelphia, J. B. Lippincott Co., 1943.

Jacobs, Bruce, *Heroes of the Army*, New York, W. W. Norton & Co., Inc., 1956.

Mackenzie, DeWitt, *Men Without Guns*, Philadelphia, The Blakiston Company, 1945.

White, W. L., *Back Down the Ridge*, New York, Harcourt Brace and Company, 1953.

U.S. GOVERNMENT PUBLICATIONS

"Above and Beyond the Call of Duty," Medal of Honor, The Navy, 1950, Prepared by the Bureau of Naval Personnel.

243

Curriculum for U.S. Naval School Deep Sea Divers, Bureau of Naval Personnel, Washington, D.C., 20370, April 1964.

History of the Medical Department of the U.S. Navy in World War II, NAVMER P-5031 Vol. I, and NAVMED P-5021 Vol. II, U.S. Government Printing Office, Washington, D.C., 1953.

Medal of Honor Recipients, 1863–1963, Prepared for the Subcommittee on Veterans' Affairs of the Committee on Labor and Public Welfare, United States Senate, U.S. Government Printing Office, Washington, D.C., 1964.

Medical and Dental Support, FMFM 4–5, Department of the Navy, Hq. U.S. Marine Corps, Washington, D.C., 20380. U.S. Government Printing Office, October, 1963.

Medical Support of the Army Air Forces in World War II (prepared by Mae Mills Link and Hubert A. Coleman), Office of the Surgeon General, USAF, U.S. Government Printing Office, Washington, D.C., 1955.

U.S. Navy Diving Manual, Navy Department, Washington 25, D.C. U.S. Government Printing Office, July, 1963.

PERIODICALS

The Airman: "New Look in Air Force Medicine," August 1960; "Meet the Man in the White Smock," February, 1964.

All Hands: "Medics in Training," July, 1952; "Hospital Corpsmen on the Field of Combat," February, 1958; "How Did It Start—Hospital Corpsmen," July, 1960; "Outpost Against Disease," November, 1962; "Country Doctor, USN, in Taiwan," April, 1964.

Army Medical Services, Ministry of Defense, London, England, 1964.

Hospital Corps Quarterly, Volume 21, Number 2, April-May-June, 1948.

Leatherneck, "Corpsman!" HMC Harold B. Rice, April, 1950.

Medical Service Digest, "Increased Airman Specialization," May, 1965.

Naval Institute Proceedings, "Combat Swimmers," Watts and Ritter, May, 1965.

Navy Times, "Navy Trains Disease Fighters," HMC Harold B. Rice, December 18, 1954.

Our Navy, "Bring Those Casualties Back!" HMC Harold B. Rice, August 1, 1955.

Index

247